Odyssey of Courage

Odyssey of Courage

THE STORY OF
Alvar Núñez Cabeza de Vaca

MAIA WOJCIECHOWSKA

Decorations by Alvin Smith

ATHENEUM   1966   NEW YORK

Copyright © 1965 by Maia Wojciechowska
Library of Congress catalog card number: 65–10477
Published simultaneously in Canada by McClelland & Stewart Ltd.
Manufactured in the United States of America
Printed by Halliday Lithograph Corporation,
West Hanover, Massachusetts
Bound by H. Wolff, New York
Designed by David Rogers
First printing January 1965
Second printing March 1966
Third printing June 1966

"To one who went into the world well loved."

Introduction

It was the end of an era.

Toward the close of the fifteenth century and at the beginning of the sixteenth, new worlds exploded out of the darkness of the unknown.

The modern age was being born in Florence. A renaissance of the arts brought new life to men's minds. Questioning began. Men refused to continue to accept everything on faith. Their minds were reaching upward and outward like freed birds.

Although Italy was the birthplace of modern man, it was Spain that gave him a whole new continent. At the end of the fifteenth century, Spain was a country plagued by poverty and endless wars, hunger and despair. Its major problem was the Moors. But a man's mind invented a new weapon, artillery. With it the Spaniards were finally able to expell the Moors from Granada, their last stronghold, and King Ferdinand could proudly declare:

"We have united a country
but we must yet mold a nation."

As he gave reluctant permission to Christopher Columbus to prove or disprove his theory that a sea route to the Indies would be shorter than an overland route, the King did not know that Spain was about to begin its domination of two empires: Europe and new lands across the Atlantic.

At two o'clock on the morning of October 12, 1492, a nameless lookout on the small vessel *Pinta*, sighted the white sands of a beach. With the discovery of Española, the shape of the world changed dramatically. And so did the aspirations of men.

Inflamed by the promise of gold and the lure of the unknown, Spaniards began to sail west. Juan de Solís, Cortés, Balboa, Pedro de Mendoza, Juan Ponce de Leon —adventurers, heroes, pathfinders—became a new brand of men. Exposed to danger and hardship beyond imagination, they hardened in heart as well as body.

It was a time of glory and a time of incredible adventures; a time that turned pious men into tyrants and tyrant kings into slaves. It was a time of superhuman courage and inhuman behavior; a time of discovery, not only of new lands and strange people, but also of the bitter depths of human nature. It was a time of the legendary El Dorado, a never-found kingdom of a golden man; a time of mirages and of realities stranger than visions; a time of madness; a time of greed; a time of hunger and of looting; a time of pride; a time of daring feats. It was also a time when, in the name of Christ, whole nations were annihilated; a time when Christianity was triumphant, but Christ had much to be ashamed of in the things that were done in his name.

In half a man's lifetime, after 1492, Spain discovered and conquered all of Central and part of South America.

Only the continent of North America remained unexplored. The man who began the penetration of that unknown was like no other of the conquistadors. His name was Alvar Núñez Cabeza de Vaca.

The author wishes to acknowledge her great debt to Mr. Morris Bishop, whose excellent book, *The Odyssey of Cabeza de Vaca* (Century, N.Y. 1933) was not only the inspiration for this one, but also served as an important source of information, along with Cabeza de Vaca's own *Relatión*.

The author took "fictitious" liberty with only two characters: the Gypsy and Domingo Martínez. Both existed and have been referred to in books on Cabeza de Vaca, but information about them is very scant. The author chose not to mention Cabeza de Vaca's wife because information about her is almost nonexistent.

Dialogue, which occurs infrequently, is of course, imaginary, but in each instance is based on facts; these facts have been transformed into speeches.

The route taken by Cabeza de Vaca and his companions is a matter for speculation. The author gives more credibility to the Hallenbeck and Sauer theory. According to them, the four men travelled over parts of five states: Florida, Texas, New Mexico, Arizona and California. According to other sources, Cabeza de Vaca's route was more coastal.

Maia Wojciechowska
Oakland, N. J.

PART I

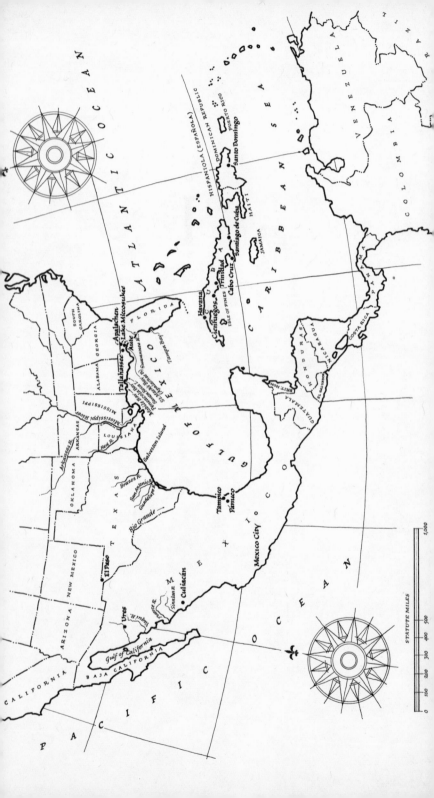

"He would have done it! He would have kissed the hand of Cortés!"

"Not Pánfilo de Nárvaez! Never!"

"But that's what I heard from a man who was there. Cortés had Nárvaez imprisoned for three years; and when he let him go, Nárvaez humbled himself in front of the conqueror of Mexico."

"Whether it happened or not is not important. The fact is that Cortés is a great man, a true military genius, and Nárvaez is nothing more than an opportunist. He *should* have bowed to the boldest of all conquistadors. Was there ever, I ask you, a man who could conquer a whole kingdom with only 450 men and 20 horses?"

"And that conquest went to his head. Nárvaez was

sent to conquer the conqueror!"

"With 1,400 men! And what did he accomplish?"

"Nothing! He lost an eye; his men deserted to Cortés; and he himself became a prisoner."

"But Nárvaez is a cunning man. He might have pretended to humble himself in front of Cortés. Now he has come to Spain to testify against Cortés at the Council of the Indies."

"Have you heard about that mare of his, that monster of a horse he has in Cuba?"

"He trained that mare to kick with her front and her back legs, killing the savages right and left; but she never unseats her master."

"Cortés unseated him!"

"I heard that one night, during an Indian raid—and there must have been several thousand redskins attacking—Nárvaez, dressed in his nightshirt, tied some cowbells to his mare's saddle and, alone, rode out to meet the Indians. He routed them alone, sent them right back to the jungle. All alone! He and his mare!"

"No one says he is not a brave man. Anyone in His Majesty's service for twenty years, especially in the Indies, could not survive if he were not brave."

"He is well known for his courage and endurance. Some even say that he is an honest man. But what he is really known for is his hatred of the heathen and his brutality towards them."

"Las Casas, accused him of that."

"Why shouldn't he? He was with Nárvaez on one of those expeditions he undertook to wipe out the natives. Father Las Casas told me himself how it was. The natives were friendly, offering food to Nárvaez, when

4

one of his soldiers drew out a sword and beheaded an Indian. In less time than it takes to say two Credos, the Spaniards killed all the natives. Las Casas said that Nárvaez just sat there, on his mare, and watched, not moving a muscle, not saying anything."

"He is a good man, that priest."

"Nárvaez is a better man. He kills the savages and brings riches back to Spain."

"He gets rich himself, you mean. And he dreams of nothing but getting richer and richer."

"He came to Spain to testify against Cortés, not to get rich."

"Everyone knows he came back to get the King's permission to explore Florida. The riches there are said to be even greater than those in Mexico."

"Haven't you heard? The King had already granted him permission. He will be governor of all the lands he explores. He is supposed to colonize and pacify the region known as Florida."

"Has he pacified Cuba? He knows one thing: how to kill the natives. What are we going to do with all that new land if there is nobody left to cultivate it? Are we all to become serfs in the Indies? Is that why we conquered, to go back to sowing and plowing?"

"Nárvaez will make the natives work the land. He himself will establish permanent settlements, and he will build three forts. There will be no working there, just supervision."

"He will hunt for gold and forget everything else. I've heard him talk. He is saying that he wants his riches to surpass those of Cortés. He wants to govern a land so big that Mexico will seem like his back yard."

A man called Alvar Núñez Cabeza de Vaca listened intently whenever anyone talked about Nárvaez. He knew that Nárvaez had been granted permission to explore Florida, and he, Cabeza de Vaca, wanted, more than anything else, to be part of that expedition. If ever, he thought, he was going to make the voyage across the Atlantic, it would have to be now. Narvaez's expedition was the only one setting out soon.

He had not been, in his thirty-five years, a stranger to danger. In 1511 he had sailed with an expeditionary force to Italy. Pope Julius II, unable to cope with one of the everlasting wars that broke out like brush fire on the Italian peninsula, had asked King Ferdinand for help. Cabeza de Vaca, then in the King's service, had been among those sent.

Thirteen years later, the memory of the bloody battle of Ravenna was still vivid. On the field that April day in 1512, twenty thousand men were killed. The Spaniards had lost the battle. The French, whom they had fought, were victorious, but had suffered such heavy losses, including the death of their leader, that they were obliged to leave Italy altogether.

Cabeza de Vaca still did not know by what miracle he had been among the few whose lives had been spared. For a long time afterward his dreams had been rife with the memory of slaughter. With the passing of time, the conviction had grown up in him that God had had a purpose in sparing him. And yet he did not know, could not imagine, what that purpose might be.

He had had no heart for further wars upon his return to Spain. And so he married and entered the services of the Duke of Medina. As a *camarero*, a steward, he

6

was expected to undertake the duties of a peacetime soldier, tasks befitting a gentleman and not a butcher. But there was no peace. On September 16, 1520, some commoners, discontented over taxes, rose in rebellion and seized the Duke's castle. The following day Cabeza de Vaca, at the Duke's side, was fighting the rebels. The Duke's forces recaptured the stronghold, and as his reward, Cabeza de Vaca was promoted to Commander of the City Gate. But even in this job there was bloodshed. Again and again he had to fight the rebels and the French.

It was not that he wanted quiet. He had always been restless, restless for adventure. But his hunger for it was not appeased by war. Ever since, as a boy, he had heard his explorer grandfather talk of the strange lands of the Canaries, ever since he had watched the first sailors return from the Indies, he had dreamed of exploring the unknown. He wanted that kind of danger: the danger of wilderness and the challenge of the unfamiliar.

As he sat in the public gallery watching the Council of the Indies investigate Cortés, Cabeza de Vaca saw and listened to the man with whom he was determined to sail to the New World.

Nárvaez was very tall and gave the appearance of having tremendous physical strength. His limbs were like those of a sturdy tree. His long face ended in a thick, wiry, red beard. His one eye darted everywhere, but could also focus with a penetrating gaze. When he spoke, his voice had an arresting depth, and in anger it exploded up from the soles of his shoes. Cabeza de Vaca knew before long that this man could never be his friend. There was too much cunning in his words, too much stubbornness in his thoughts, too much cruelty behind his eye. But Cabeza de Vaca was not looking for a friend; he was looking for a way to reach the Indies.

"I'll help you," Father Las Casas said after a moment's silence. "I'll intercede for you with the King. But—" his dark eyes flashed and his hands came together, not in prayer, but in a gesture of determination,— "you must realize that it was I who drew up the provisions Nárvaez must obey. And you, if you are made treasurer of the expedition, must uphold them with your life, if necessary. I know Nárvaez. I know his treatment of the natives. There must not be—" he raised his voice, "—there cannot be, a repetition of the senseless slaughter that took place in Cuba. You must see to it that the natives are given their rights as human beings."

Cabeza de Vaca was surprised at the passion in the voice of the priest.

"If there is any brutality," the priest went on, his eyes fastened on the young nobleman, "you must report it immediately. Your reports will be passed on to the Council of the Indies, and the guilty ones will be severely punished. Any Indian, no matter how savage you may think him, is entitled to be treated as a free man as long as he is obedient and pays his annual tribute to the Crown. No one, except the most rebellious ones, can be made slaves. And the decision as to whom is to be considered rebellious will belong not to Nárvaez but to the priests on his expedition."

The penetrating gaze of the priest never left Cabeza de Vaca's face. He felt that he was passing a test, and evidently passing it well. For the priest continued: "I know that cunning wolf, Nárvaez, is going to laugh at the provision. He will laugh and think them naïve and the King's instructions ignorant. He will try to tell you that neither the King nor you is familiar with the conditions among the redskins, that the sword is the only language they understand. But remember that it is I who wrote those provisions. And I am familiar with the Indians, with the conditions among them. You must not be fooled by Nárvaez. We cannot afford any longer to conquer people by enslaving some and killing the rest. We must respect human rights, human lives, the dignity of man. For if we do not respect that, we do not respect Christ himself. When you look at the face of a savage, a face which may be smeared with the blood of pagan sacrifice, I want you to see in it Christ's own face."

There was no doubt, Cabeza de Vaca thought, listening to the priest, that the words he heard were those of a good man. But only an idealist or a fanatic would think that way. After all, he, Cabeza de Vaca, had met a score of explorers and discoverers, and not one of them had been worried about the natives. But if instructions for such behavior were incorporated into the King's decree and if he were treasurer and enforcer of those instructions, he would do as he was told.

It was because of his known honesty, his remarkable integrity, his mathematical ability, and his indifference to wealth, that King Charles V did appoint Cabeza de Vaca treasurer of the Nárvaez expedition. To give him additional authority, the King also made him provost marshal, a job that placed him in charge of military discipline.

While Nárvaez was scouting the countryside for men to join his expedition, promising them glory in the conversion of pagans and riches in conquest beyond all imagination, he was also saving money by buying old, inadequate ships. He bought five of them: five vessels that some thought could only be held together on the high seas by prayer. He borrowed money everywhere, promising the lenders a share in his coming wealth. With this money he purchased provisions, but only from merchants who were willing to part with their goods for a song or for a piece of paper entitling them to a share of the gold that would be found in Florida. He also managed to persuade quite a few of his crew, many of them wealthy adventurers, to sell him their fine clothes. "In the tropics," he said, "you need nothing but your own skins." Having purchased the clothes, he resold them to men he could not recruit for his expedition.

While Nárvaez was haggling and getting things ready in Sanlúcar de Barrameda, Cabeza de Vaca made a short trip to Jerez de la Frontera, the town of his childhood. He walked through the streets of the town, remembering things long forgotten, words spoken when he was a small boy. He visited the house where his mother had lived and died. He peeked through the windows of the school, where he had once sat, impatiently waiting for classes to end, so that he could rush off to his grandfather's house, and hear stories of the Canary Islands. His grandfather had died when he was only eleven, but the memory of the times they had spent together was still very vivid. He could still hear the old man's voice:

"I hope you will take courage as your mate, and adventure as your companion."

He was about to do that. He wished his grandfather were alive now, seeing him off, advising him, teaching him. But if he were alive, he would only laugh at the provisions about the treatment of Indians. "They're animals," he would probably shout.

Finally, on June 17, 1527, the five vessels slowly left the Sanlúcar pier. Relatives and friends of the men on board gathered to see them off. Worried by the condition of the ships, the visitors prayed aloud for the safety of the departing adventurers.

"Did you hear the creaking?"

"How could I help but hear? I am not deaf."

"Even a deaf person could hear."

"Why did they have to cram them so tight?"

"It's too expensive otherwise. Nárvaez had to finance everything himself. All these adventurers have to pay their own way."

"They're more saints than adventurers."

"Saints or adventurers, they need all the praying we can give them."

"How many men are there?"

"Six hundred."

"Ten of them have wives with them."

"Did you see the horses being loaded?"

"Yes. They were all Andalusian breed."

"In the Indies a horse is worth more than ten men."

"Why do you blaspheme?"

"It's true! Without horses they could never conquer the savages. The Indians have never seen horses. They think a man on horseback is a monster."

"They also took pigs, cows and goats with them."

"The animals will be more comfortable than the people."

"Don't forget the sheep. They also took sheep."

"Do you speak of men or animals?"

"In this case, animals."

"My son sold Nárvaez a beautiful cape and a doublet. The boy left with no clothes but those he had on his back."

"They had no space for luggage."

"What space there is, is occupied by the rats."

"They are as big as pigs."

"Bigger."

"Thank God I am not with them on those leaky vessels."

"They just creaked, they didn't leak."

"Maybe not now, but they will. Nárvaez certainly didn't go overboard, spending for the expedition."

"The reason he's so rich is that he keeps what he has. It must be from the Indians that he learned to be thrifty, no Spaniard could teach him that."

"One learns nothing from the Indians. Nárvaez was born in Valladolid. Those who come from there are born that way."

"God forbid that his stinginess should kill them all."

Those on board the vessels soon discovered for themselves how very true it was that Nárvaez was stingy. The food supply was extremely poor in quality, and its quantity was quite insufficient for six hundred people. Only the cockroaches, which attacked the meager rations, seem to thrive. The passengers, or at least those not sick enough to stop eating, were allotted a pound-and-a-half of biscuit a day and a quart of wine. On Mondays, Wednesdays, Fridays, and Saturdays, there was bean and chick-pea soup and a third-of-a-pound of

12

salt fish. Each Sunday and Thursday a pound of meat and two ounces of cheese were distributed per person. On Tuesday, the never varying menu included rice soup, two ounces of salt pork and oil. Nárvaez himself, however, had a table provided with a variety of more tasteful dishes: fowl, roast pork, green vegetables, fruits and cheeses, not to mention pastry and vintage wines.

The vessels, themselves, much too small for an ocean crossing, were high-pooped, high-forecastled, top-heavy crafts that pitched and rolled with every wave even on the calmest sea. And the leaks were there, necessitating continuous bailing by the crew. The space allotted the passengers was no greater than that given the penned livestock. On deck there was no space to stand, let alone to sit, comfortably. Any sort of exercise, such as walking, was out of the question. Seasickness was commonplace and completely impossible to hide. The only way to get clean was to stand windward and let the sea spray act as a shower. Lack of even the most primitive sanitation soon brought fleas to challenge the domination of the ships by the rats and the cockroaches.

The leaders of the expedition had all been appointed by the King, as Cabeza de Vaca had been. Besides Cabeza de Vaca, there was a Franciscan father, Juan Suárez, who headed a group of five priests. Father Suárez was not a novice in the Indies; he had been with Cortés in Mexico. The post of assessor was held by Alonso de Solís; the comptroller was Alonso Enríquez. This was the complete staff, aside from Nárvaez.

The expedition made a brief stop in Tenerife, in the Canaries. As Cabeza de Vaca looked at the steep, savage mountains, the smoke of volcanoes billowing above, he was filled again with memories of his childhood and memories of his grandfather. Pedro de Vera: the conqueror and governor of the Canaries; the fighter of Moors and master of savages. As a boy, Cabeza de Vaca had not known his grandfather until after he retired. But the old warrior had been interested still in new worlds and what they had to offer; so the two, the boy and the grandfather, had been among the first in Spain to taste of pineapples and sweet potatoes; and they had been among the first to hear news from across the Atlantic. They had spent hours sitting with the sailors in the harbor, listening to their tales of savage new lands where man-eating Indians were trying to resist the invasion of white men bearing crosses and swords. The two had seen the faces of those who came back, faces hardened by privation and terror. The eyes of those who came back were different from the eyes of those who went. And in that difference the boy first saw the good and the bad inside men's souls. Now he was learning more: learning from the greed of Nárvaez and from the deprived men who served under him.

The stop in the Canaries was not long enough for those who had become deathly sick of the sea. Amid grumbling and threats, the five ships sailed on. The crossing took two months, and each day the nightmare grew.

When they finally arrived at the lush, green shores of the island of Española, 140 men deserted the expedition the minute the plank was lowered.

2

"I've lost a quarter of my men!" Nárvaez shouted in anger.

"The voyage was made more difficult," Cabeza de Vaca said, "by the lack of proper provisions. The men were disillusioned."

He wanted to add that he had overheard the men voice their distrust of Nárvaez. There was a general dislike for his personality and those who deserted preferred to remain poor if necessary, anywhere, than to go on with Nárvaez toward the riches of Florida.

"It's easy for you to talk." Nárvaez's one eye glared. "You only had to put up a small bond; I, on the other hand, had to spend a small fortune."

Cabeza de Vaca knew Nárvaez to be a rich man.

Furthermore, his provisions stated that he was to receive an annual salary of fifty thousand maravedís, the equivalent of $1,000. And beyond this, four percent of all taxes from the new lands were to go to him. If Florida proved to be as rich as everyone anticipated, this would amount to a fortune. He could also select a piece of land, 400,000 acres, for himself and his family. But he was now, as he had been in Spain, preoccupied by his imagined lack of money.

"Santo Domingo is no place," Nárvaez complained bitterly, "to get anything! I can't get recruits here. Those deserters will soon regret their cowardly deed. Here they'll be living among thieves. They're all thieves here, in Santo Domingo! Every merchant I've approached for supplies has tried to bleed me dry!"

"But, we cannot," Cabeza de Vaca reminded him, "put out without adequate supplies. And since we've lost quite a few horses, we should also replace those."

"All I am prepared to buy here is a small ship. And I've heard where I can get one cheap. The horses, arms, and food supplies will have to wait. We'll get what we need in Santiago de Cuba. They're fewer thieves there. I'm known in Cuba, and the merchants would be ashamed of cheating me."

For forty-five days Nárvaez raged over prices and tried unsuccessfully to bargain for the things he had to have. Meanwhile, Cabeza de Vaca took long walks through the colonial town. The island had grown prosperous since its discovery by Columbus. The town had beautiful houses, with cool patios, shaded by tropical trees. Some streets were even paved, and the lushness of the tropical vegetation covered what was only makeshift. There was much activity in Santo Domingo. In the port, where ships brought in Spanish goods and loaded exotic fruits and vegetables, and gold and diamonds, the din was as great as in any busy European port. In the saloons, sailors got drunk and fought as if they were on Spanish soil instead of surrounded by the jungles of a still barely-explored island.

The Spaniards, who were established in *encomiendas*, land grants, were dressed splendidly. They rode their Andalusian horses as if they were riding in the Easter parade in Seville. Their ladies looked happy and haughty. They may have been no more than servant girls in Spain, but here they were aristocrats.

In contrast, the Indian natives, were emaciated and defeated looking. Some were in chains, others showed marks of beatings. All were made to work hard, building or cultivating the land. Their eyes looked downward, and their gestures denoted despair. Cabeza de Vaca felt sorry for them. Until recently they, and not the Spaniards, had ruled this land.

"Why are the Indians treated so badly?" he asked one of the landowners. "Does not the King demand fair treatment for them?"

"The King is in Spain, and we are here."

"But a law . . ."

"Laws are made by us," the man said, smiling. "The strange thing about these Indians is that a lot of them would rather hang themselves than serve us. Only the other morning I rode out into a jungle being cleared by the Indians, and what do you suppose I saw? A whole family, hanging on a tree. Five of them. They killed themselves, and I didn't even have a chance to make them work for their dinner. I'd just bought them the day before."

After this conversation Cabeza de Vaca re-read the King's document requiring that no such cruelty be committed in the new lands. No native was to be converted to Christianity against his will; and no one was to be forced into slavery or made to work for the Spanish against his will. All were to be paid wages for any work that they did for the Spanish.

Re-reading the document, Cabeza de Vaca made a promise to himself that no Indian in Florida would ever have cause to commit suicide as long as he was the King's treasurer. But this was not all. He was convinced now that Las Casas was right. These were human beings; and each one was entitled to love and compassion and protection. He sent a report to the Council of the Indies, pointing out the injustices committed by the Spaniards.

Nárvaez was eager to proceed. Forty-five days had been wasted. He was in extremely bad temper then, when finally the six ships, including the small one he had at last purchased, put out for Santiago de Cuba. Since this was the hurricane season, Nárvaez was anxious to reach the safety of that port. He was also impatient to reach a land where people knew him, to return home and bask in the glory of being commander of an army that, under his leadership, was going to conquer a whole new continent. He hoped to impress many of his friends and most of the merchants, from whom he expected favorable prices. He also hoped that recruits would join his expedition, recruits with their own horses and arms.

He was lucky in all of his expectations. He got good

horses and passable supplies for his money. A group of
adventurers, with jungle experience joined him. And his
luck continued. Word reach him that in Trinidad, on the
coast of Cuba some three hundred miles to the west of
Santiago, a man was willing to give him a sizable
amount of provisions. He determined to go and get them
as soon as his business in Santiago was concluded.

While Nárvaez was carrying on his negotiations,
some of the more superstitious among his men decided
that they wanted an assurance that they had a future.
They had heard that there was an old Gypsy fortune-
teller living in Santiago de Cuba, and they hired a young
Indian to take them to the Gypsy's tent. Once she had
lived on fortune telling and on stealing in Granada. But
she had followed her own fortune, and now she did not
need to steal. Here they were willing to pay her well,
the soldiers of fortune and their ladies, who droned into
her ears their fears, uncertainty, and nightmares. She
interpreted their dreams and predicted their futures.

She didn't even need her cards when she saw
Nárvaez' men walk into her tent. Death was in their
features, the smell of it was clinging to them, and she
turned her face away from them.

"I'm busy," she said. "Come back some other day."

She herself had had a dream of many ships and many
men sailing to a new land. She had seen the ships drifting
apart and bodies in the blue of the water. And then she
had seen just four men, three white and a black, walking
through green forests. She had awakened when a bird
screamed.

The men placed money on the table and laughed.

"We want to know, even the worst," they said to

her. "We're sailing to Florida with Nárvaez, and we don't trust him. Look into the your cards and tell what's in store for us."

She closed her eyes. The heat of the tropics made her old body more tired each day. She wished she were back in Granada with her children and grandchildren, nieces and nephews, the hundred or more of her blood. She knew she would never see them again, hear their songs and see their dances. She knew she would die here.

"Come on, old woman, we haven't all day."

She shuffled the cards, the long, worn, torn cards that served her like a sword served a soldier. They were her weapon against the world.

"Cut towards you," she said to the man nearest her. "I'll tell it to you once, and once only. This will be for the whole expedition, not just your own future."

In her dream one of the men who survived had been most noble looking, a very handsome man. Before she went on, she described him, just as she had seen him in that dream, and asked his name.

"That must be Alvar Núñez Cabeza de Vaca," one of the men said. "Did he come to you?"

"Let us hear our future," another said impatiently.

The cards fell the way she knew they would. Doom was everywhere.

"You will not live," she said, her voice tired, "to conquer anything. You will all die, all but four of you, and the four are not here. The water will swallow some, and the rest will be killed by the Indians. It is a pity, a great pity; but what must be, will be."

She scooped the cards and put them in her pocket.

"What kind of fortune telling is this?" one of the

men shouted angrily.

"Each card has a meaning; why don't you tell us what you see in each card?"

"Details of death do not matter," the old Gypsy said.

"Tell us more," one of the men shouted angrily.

"There is no more," she said, watching them go out of her tent, their steps already heavy with the knowledge that they had bought. She knew they would get drunk to forget. But the next day they would remember. And they would talk, tell everyone that death awaited them. Yet, she knew, nothing would change. They would sail to Florida and meet their end there.

Nárvaez was at last ready to go for his free provisions. And he was impatient. Although advised by many against sailing because the hurricane season was near, he set off. Conditions were calm when they pulled anchor, but midway to Trinidad, the weather changed. The fleet was forced to seek shelter at Cabo Cruz.

As soon as the weather cleared, Nárvaez ordered two ships to proceed to Trinidad. He placed Cabeza de Vaca in command of one of those ships.

"The only reason," one of the pilots told Cabeza de Vaca, "that we reached Trinidad was that luck was with us. The hurricane is coming. That much I know. And luck will not protect us when it does. This port offers no shelter at all."

"I'll send thirty men ashore," Cabeza de Vaca replied. "They'll have instructions to hurry back with the supplies. I, myself, will remain aboard."

"The wind," the pilot said, scanning the skies, "is

changing. That's a bad sign. If the hurricane does come, we're done. There is no escape in this place. A dozen ships have gone down here, during a heavy blow."

Cabeza de Vaca commanded the men to get the supplies and return as fast as possible. Then he began his anxious wait. The weather became steadily worse. The wind rose and a heavy rain started to fall early the next morning. The harbor waters raised considerably.

"A canoe of Indians is coming to starboard," a lookout shouted above the wind.

Cabeza de Vaca listened to the Indians. He was needed in town. The promised provisions had to be signed for by him.

"I cannot leave the ships," he told them.

"We were told not to come back without the captain," the Indians replied.

"There is too much danger now. I cannot abandon the ships," Cabeza de Vaca insisted.

"You'd better go," the pilot, visibly frightened, advised him. "If you don't go now and hurry back, we shall all perish. There is no time to lose. Besides, you can speed up the loading of supplies just by being there."

"I shall go then," Cabeza de Vaca decided. "If the hurricane does come, beach the ships if you can. But do not think of the ships first. Think of yourselves. Save yourselves and the horses. Go to land and seek shelter."

Asking for volunteers to come with him, he found only eight. The others did not wish to venture into the torrential rains. It was far better to stay dry under cover than to go into the jungle and get soaked. Cabeza de Vaca and the eight set out alone.

"We'll go ashore tomorrow," his men shouted after

him. "Tomorrow we shall all go to Sunday Mass."

But there was no Mass that Sunday.

The hurricane screamed inland with a fury of powerful winds and a deluge from the sky. Not only the church, but almost all of the houses in Trinidad, collapsed under it. Linking hands, the men ashore escaped into the jungle, away from the flying bricks and lumber. All around the fleeing men, trees were uprooted, even stones were hurled through the air.

Huddling inside natural cavities in the earth, the survivors: Cabeza de Vaca, his eight companions, and the thirty men he had sent ashore earlier, spent the nightmarish night, as the forces of nature raged all around them. And all through that night, Cabeza de Vaca heard, he later reported, "a tumult and great clamor of voices, the sound of timbals, flutes, and tamborines, as well as other instruments." These strange noises must have come from the terrified natives who were imploring their gods to protect them.

With the coming of day, the storm subsided. Cabeza de Vaca and his men emerged from the jungle and moved toward the harbor. Their hearts sank at the sight of the fallen trees, the earth bare of grass and leaves. Everything in the path of the hurricane had been destroyed. Soon they were looking at the churning waters of the sea. The ships were gone. The men sank to their knees in prayer as they gazed at two empty buoys and some pieces of wreckage. Crying, they got up to search the shore and came across two sailors.

"The bodies," Cabeza de Vaca later wrote in his report of the disaster to the King, "were so disfigured by striking against rocks as to be unrecognizeable. There were also found a cape and a tattered quilt, nothing else."

Sixty men and twenty horses had perished. A messenger was sent by Cabeza de Vaca to bring the unhappy news to Nárvaez. The report to the King, when it was later published in Spain, became the first description by a European of a West Indian hurricane.

Although Nárvaez wanted to go on to Florida without further delay, Cabeza de Vaca told him that not one of the storm survivors was willing to risk being caught by another hurricane.

"And I am with them," he wrote, "in the decision to spend the winter in the safety of a nearby harbor. Cienfuegos, just a few miles west of here, is a safe port. There we intend to wait out the hurricane season."

Realizing that he would have no crew to sail with, Nárvaez gave up and decided to wait until spring. Cabeza de Vaca was placed in command of the men and the ships that had safely weathered the hurricane in Cabo Cruz. Nárvaez himself spent the winter with his wife. During that time he procured another ship, and hired a captain, forty infantrymen, and twelve cavalrymen. On his way to Cienfuegos, he went to Trinidad where he had heard an inexpensive ship was to be had and bought it. For it he enlisted a crew from among the settlers of the stricken town, and hired a pilot, Diego Miruelo, who swore he knew the Florida coast like the back of his hand.

It was February 1528, when Nárvaez reached Cienfuegos to check on the ships and the army under Cabeza de Vaca's command. He found the men happy and grateful for the time given them to regain their courage. They were all eager now to gain the fabulous riches of Florida.

The following day, February 20th, an order was given to hoist the sails. Four hundred and eighty men, eight with their wives, and eighty horses, boarded four ships and one brigantine and sailed out of the safe harbor of Cienfuegos Bay.

In Havana another vessel joined them. Then, under the command of the pilot Miruelo, the ships moved on toward Florida. But not for long. They soon hit a coral reef, which held them fast for fifteen days, and many of the men took this to be a forecast of even worse disaster. A storm, which caught them still imprisoned, increased their fears. The priests were busy hearing the confessions of men who were ready to die and despaired of ever reaching the Florida coast. But instead of killing them, the storm actually saved them by freeing the ships from the hold of the reef.

But this was not the end of the season of storms, and twice again the winds lashed out at them. Holy Week came and went, with the sailors much too sick or too busy trying to keep their vessels from floundering, to observe the holidays.

But finally, on April 12, the sun came out. With shouts of joy, the men hailed flocks of shore birds approaching the ships; and soon, laughing at the end of their ill-fated voyage, everyone was out on deck looking across the smooth greenness of the sea toward the more welcome greenness of mangrove islands. This was the coast! The coast of the new land. The coast of Florida.

3

The waters of the Florida lagoon where the ships anchored, were calm. In front of the ships, a land of marshes, oaks, and palms made a tight band of green. Further to the east, beyond large, sun-bleached mounds of oyster shells, the men could see an Indian village.

The natives did not come forward to either greet them or threaten them. So Alonso Enríques was sent ashore as emissary to assure the Indians of the good intentions of their new governor. The chief made an offering of venison and fish, but Enríques left convinced that the Indians did not trust him. As he came aboard to report this to Nárvaez, the entire population of the village fled into the forest. The Spaniards went ashore and excitedly explored the little huts, certain of finding precious stones, silver, and gold. They were greatly disappointed. The Indians seemed to have no possessions and left no food behind. However, one of the men did discover, in the tangle of fish nets, a child's gold rattle.

"If they give a baby gold to play with," the men said among themselves, "they must truly have mountains of it. We shall all be rich."

On April 16, 1528, Nárvaez took formal possession of Florida in a ceremony full of protocol. First, the Spanish flag was raised, and alongside it, the priests planted a wooden cross. Then Nárvaez, dressed in his court clothes, read the *Requerimiento*, a lengthy proclamation of peaceful conquest. If any of the Timucua Indians witnessed the ceremony and heard the words, they lay hidden in the swamp grass understanding nothing. In other parts of the New World conquered by Spain, at least a pretense had been made of having a few natives present. Here, the words were read to the swaying trees and the singing birds, to the blue sky and the whispering wind, to the placid waters and to the assembled Spaniards. The notary in his report, like all notaries present at similar occasions, certified that the proper information as to the state of their bodies, souls and land, had been given to the natives and that Florida now belonged to the Crown.

The pomposity of the occasion was marred on the return to the ships by the need to dump overboard the rotting carcasses of thirty-eight dead horses. The death of these horses was a great blow to Nárvaez. The forty-two that had survived the trip from Cuba were led out of the ships, and swaying feebly on their legs, sent to graze gratefully on the tough marsh grass. They were too weak after the sea voyage to be of any use to the men, although the sight of them on the grassy slopes of the new land made the Spaniards smile with expectation. There were wild jungles ahead and a fierce sea behind, but the Gypsy's prophesy had not been fulfilled. They were alive and well.

The next day, Easter Sunday, a solemn high Mass was celebrated in a spirit of gratefulness and hope. Shortly after, while the men, having eaten fresh seafood, were resting and enjoying the peacefulness of the day, several Indians appeared out of the bush. The naked men confronted Nárvaez. Their gestures indicated plainly that they wished the Spaniards to leave. Their language was incomprehensible, but Nárvaez laughed at the passion in their eyes, at the anger in their faces. He toyed with the idea that he could kill the emissaries and show those who had sent them that he was master here, that his was the power to command. But instead, he chose to ignore them. He was not interested in the natives; not yet, not until he had a chance to see for himself what kind of land they inhabited, what sort of a country he now owned.

Early the next morning, thirty-four men on foot and six men mounted on the still-exhausted horses followed Nárvaez and Cabeza de Vaca on the first inland reconnaissance trip. They traveled northeast for ten miles, reaching Tampa Bay, which their pilot knew about but had been unsuccessful in locating. The men did not realize what they were seeing however. They mistook the wide mouth of the harbor for the sea. And the Bay remained undiscovered.

Unimpressed by the land, yet encouraged by the absence of hostile natives, Nárvaez turned back to order the pilot, Miruelo, to sail the smallest ship northward in search of a safe harbor. Should he fail to find one, he was to proceed to Havana and bring back another ship full of provisions. Since the first offering of fish and deer, the Spaniards had found nothing with which to reinforce their dwindling supply of food. They had not come to a new continent to fish or hunt; they had come to find riches, and they expected the natives to provide for all their needs.

The next day Nárvaez and a handful of men set off once again to explore. As they walked through the thick vegetation along the coast, one of the horsemen saw a few natives cautiously following the expedition. Nárvaez had them captured. Showing the Indians a handful of corn, the Governor demanded to know where it came from. Unprotesting, the Indians led the Spaniards to their village. There the corn was still unripe in the fields, but the Spaniards, for the first time, took an unhurried look at the Timucua Indians. They were "of good stature, well shaped of body as any people in the world, very gently and courteous, and good natured, of tawny color, hawked nose and of pleasant countenance." [1] The women wore dresses fashioned from Spanish moss, the men covered their bodies with painted deerskins. Some had tattoo designs in azure, red, and black pigments, scratched with thorns beneath their skin. These were so artistically done that "the best painters of Europe could not improve upon them." [2] Both men and women wore inflated fish bladders in their pierced ears. The bladders were colored and glistened like pearls.

[1] Jean Ribaut wrote in 1662
[2] Jean Ribaut

But even more amazing to Nárvaez than the unexpected decorations was the discovery of several Spanish-made articles inside the Indian village. Where did the plumed hats, shoes, cloth, canvas, and iron utensils come from? The Indians pantomimed to indicate that a ship had been wrecked in the bay. There were also several wooden cases, of the kind used in Spain for packing; and in each of these the Spaniards discovered an Indian corpse, wrapped in painted deerskins. The sight of the bodies terrified some of the Spanish and appalled the priest. This pagan practice of not burying the dead had to be discouraged if the natives were to become Christians. The cases were piled outside the huts and set afire.

But the articles and the corpses were not all that the Spaniards found. There was also some gold! It was true that the pieces found were very small; but gold was gold, and there must be more of it wherever it came from. To the feverish questioning of Nárvaez came the answer: "Apalachen."

Fingers pointed to the north. There was not only gold in that province but also everything else the Spaniards might need: ripe corn and precious stones, animals and friendly people.

The time had come for Nárvaez to organize a large scale expedition into the interior. He now knew his destination: the North. Apalachen, the gold country!

The men and horses had been resting for eight days. The Indians had not made any unfriendly gestures and contented themselves with spying on the invaders from the nearby swamp. There seemed to be no reason why the Spaniards could not move on.

After dinner, the day they returned from the expedition, Nárvaez summoned Cabeza de Vaca; Alaniz, the notary; Father Suárez; Enríques; and de Solís.

"The men and I are restless," Nárvaez told them, smiling. "I propose we get on with it. We shall start off on foot to find a bay for the ships and then proceed to Apalachen."

"That would be foolish," Cabeza de Vaca said. And the smile disappeared from Nárvaez' face. "We're short of supplies, and the horses are not well enough to negotiate the wildness."

Nárvaez lowered his eye. He could not dismiss this man as he would an ordinary meddler.

"We can," Nárvaez said, controlling his temper, "get what we need from the natives along the way."

"We have seen their poverty," Cabeza de Vaca reminded the Governor.

"I've seen their gold!"

He had not meant to shout. But Cabeza de Vaca had always angered him. He had never liked this man who was forever questioning his orders and making suggestions.

"The Indians told us," Cabeza de Vaca said, "that the pieces came from up north. But how far north? We don't know how large Florida is. We don't even know if we might not be standing on a whole new continent."

"Now it is you who sound foolish," Nárvaez said mockingly.

"And could it not be," Cabeza de Vaca continued, as if he had not heard, "that the natives got those small pieces of gold from the wreckage of the Spanish ship?"

"Spanish gold!" Nárvaez leaned back and roared

with laughter. As suddenly as he started, he stopped and asked sarcastically, "From Seville, perhaps?"

"Perhaps," Cabeza de Vaca murmured. "However, my objection is not to the search for gold. We certainly should look for it, and should also remember that we have been ordered to establish settlements. But we are not yet ready for either. We are not prepared for any expedition inland at the moment. We should not leave the safety of the ships to venture across an unknown land where we are unable to communicate with the natives until . . ."

"What do you propose, then?" Nárvaez shouted, not caring now if his anger did show. "That we buy maps and hire guides? Or that we wait here until someone else makes the way safe? Or perhaps we should first of all establish a school for the natives and teach them Spanish, so that we can carry on lengthy conversations about the weather! After all, we don't want to get caught in the rain in this strange country."

When he finally stopped shouting, his one eye was bloodshot with anger and a rivulet of spittle shone on his red beard.

The notary, Alaniz, spoke up: "I agree with Alvar Núñez," he said. "I think we should wait for the pilot to come back with the supplies or news of a safe harbor. At least, we should explore from the sea first, and not from the land."

"You, too?" Nárvaez boomed at the notary. "You suggest we wait? For how long? And what do I tell my men? Don't eat while you are waiting; hold on to your empty bellies and be cautious about it?" He got up and began to pace angrily in front of them. "What do you two know of conquest? You were tucking bibs under your chins while I was marching through the wilds of Cuba." His eye searched out Father Suárez, who had spent years in Mexico. "Father, you tell them! Did Cortés wait? I've spent twenty-six years of my life in the Indies, and they were not spent waiting. And you, Father, did you wait?"

"No, one cannot afford to wait," the priest said. "I agree with the Governor, we should go by land."

Cabeza de Vaca listened, but was not convinced. He had heard the men talk about the Gypsy's prophesy and had dismissed it with a smile. He was not a superstitious man, but now he felt like one. What these two were proposing was folly.

"I am not," he said firmly, "a veteran of either Cuba or Mexico, but I have been to the wars. And going into an unknown country is not unlike going into battle. We must have an established line of communication and supplies. That is the basic requirement for any advance."

Nárvaez laughed, long and loud. The men gathered around the camp fires abandoned them and stood in the shadows listening. When Nárvaez spoke, his words were clear and his tone commanding.

"I'll lead my men northward by land. The ships will sail in search of a safe harbor. Once the harbor is found, they will make contact with the land force."

He is mad, Cabeza de Vaca thought suddenly. Aloud he asked: "How will you know the whereabouts of the ships?"

"Don't worry." Nárvaez dismissed the question with a wave of his hand. "We'll send scouts periodically."

"Under no circumstances," Cabeza de Vaca's voice trembled now, "should we leave the ships until we locate a harbor for them."

"I have," Nárvaez said coldly, "already expressed my wishes and my orders."

"In that case," Cabeza de Vaca said, his voice strong once again, "I want the notary to draw up a certificate testifying that I object strongly, both to your wishes and to your orders."

Nárvaez looked at Cabeza de Vaca for a long while. His face softened.

"I shall leave *you* in command of the ships!" His voice was mocking. "I shall leave you in charge of the women and all others who might feel safer on water than on land. You shall be in charge of the general safety."

Cabeza de Vaca's hand shot to his sword. He had been insulted. All those who heard Nárvaez, and by now a large group of the men had gathered around, understood that he had been called a coward.

"I would rather venture my life," he said calmly, "than put my honor in such a pass. As His Majesty's treasurer, it is my duty to follow you. But it is death that you have chosen, not conquest of land or discovery of gold, but death."

He stood up and walked alone into the dark woods. His own words of doom followed him like an echo.

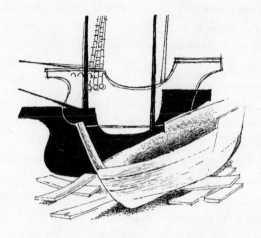

4

A handful of men and women watched from ships as the expedition set forth. It consisted of 260 on foot and 40 more on horses. They formed the first overland expedition to march into the area that is now the United States. The staccatto sound of a drum frightened the birds as the men and the horses moved forward, banners flying, armor shining in the sun, silks and plumes and leather boots gleaming through the high reeds. They were a proud-looking group. But soon the jungle thickened, and the branches began to tear at their clothing, bloodying their hands and faces. The mud dirtied their fine clothes and soft boots. The silence of the unexplored land was interrupted only by the shrill cries of wild birds, the sole inhabitants it seemed. The men worried about their meager supplies: two pounds of biscuit and half a pound of bacon for each. Many felt frightened by the silence around them; others tried to joke among themselves, but the countryside—eerie with ancient cypress trees, endless thickets, and oozing mud—was a wasteland where jokes sounded hollow. Soon, besides the birds, the men saw snakes and spiders and alligators.

Under the broiling noonday sun, the men felt as if they were being cooked alive in their armor and their silks. But they did not dare to shed them because the insects were more merciless than the heat. Clouds of mosquitoes, gnats, and flies swarmed about them constantly. Their faces were soon swollen grotesquely, welts covering every piece of exposed flesh; the men scratched until their hands dripped with their own blood. It was even impossible to breathe without inhaling the buzzing torturers. The horses fared even worse; their necks and shoulders were raw with wounds, and insects nestled inside the sores eating away the animals' strength and courage.

For fifteen days the Spaniards continued through this Florida of swamps and lakes and jungles. They saw no Indians and lived for those fifteen days on their ration of biscuits and bacon. They swayed on their feet; and when they did not pray, they swore under their breath.

"Finally," as Cabeza de Vaca wrote years later, "there came to us a chief, whom an Indian carried on his shoulders. He wore a painted deerskin, and many people followed him, and he was preceded by many players on flutes made of reeds. . . . We gave him beads and little bells and other trinkets while he presented the Governor

36

with the hide he wore." [1]

The Indian chief offered to help the Spaniards find Apalachen. He wanted to be a part of the Spanish assault on the town. So it was an enlarged army that moved on to the Suwannee, a river of swift current and dangerous depth. And there, while crossing it, the first Spaniard met his death. This first casualty was due more to impatience than to anything else. A cavalryman named Juan Velázquez could not wait for the others, who were going to cross the river on rafts; he rode his horse into the water and was immediately swept off his mount. He held onto the reins, drowning his horse as well as himself. The body of Velázquez was recovered and given a Christian burial. His horse was skinned and cooked.

Whether it was the sight of the burial, the feast on horse flesh, or simply a change of mind, no one knew, but at this time the Indian chief and his warriors suddenly withdrew. Once again the Spaniards had to cope with the wilderness alone. It soon developed, however, that they were not really alone. One of the soldiers, barely missed being killed by an arrow, the first shot aimed at the Spaniards. The Indians had not left, after all; instead they seemed to lurk behind every tree, spying silently on the desperate invaders.

[1] From: *The Journey of Alvar Núñez Cabeza de Vaca and his Companions from Florida to the Pacific, 1528-1536, Translated from his own Narrative* by Fanny Bandelier (A. S. Barnes & Co., 1905).

All material found in quotes, with the exception of conversations, in Part I of this book will be from the above source or from Buckingham Smith's translation entitled, *Narrative of Alvar Núñez Cabeza de Vaca* (George Riggs, Washington, D.C., 1851).

Nárvaez, tamed by the trying days in the wilderness, now admitted that he could never find Apalachen by himself. At the same time, finding it assumed a tremendous importance to him. Once there, he was sure he would truly be the master of this savage land.

Three Indians were captured and made to serve as guides. They, Cabeza de Vaca wrote, "led us into a country difficult to traverse and strange to look at, for it had very great forests, the trees being wonderfully tall and so many of them fallen that they obstructed our way so that we had to make long detours and with great trouble."

By the time they reached Apalachen, they had traversed three hundred miles of unexplored land in a period of fifty-five days. But the dream they had so steadfastly pursued though the wilderness, through hunger and hardships, shattered before them. No immigrant coming to New York expecting to find streets paved with gold was ever more disappointed than Nárvaez and his men were as they looked at the town of Apalachen. They had anticipated a city to rival the glory that Cortéz had found in Mexico; instead they saw on the shore of Lake Miccosukee forty thatched huts, dirty and deserted.

The sight broke Nárvaez's spirit. Much of his wealth was gone, gone to equip the expedition. The land he had marched through, almost all swampland, was valueless to him—an impassable jungle, totally useless for cultivation. The natives were too sparse to hope for any profit from slavery, even if they were meek enough to enslave painlessly, which he doubted. His own men were feeble, bloody, and sick in body and in spirit. He had led them through purgatory pursuing a mirage.

The awful prospect of a trek back through the inferno and heat; the shattered hopes of wealth; the irony of being governor of a worthless land; the sight of his men, too weak even to defend themselves from the ever-present insects and too furious to express their disappointment in words; made Nárvaez, for the first time in his life, aware of his shortcomings as a leader.

The only thing the men could do was try to regain their strength and then turn back. But first they needed food and rest. The town of Apalachen had to be captured. Nárvaez ordered Cabeza de Vaca, de Solís, and the best of the cavalrymen to take the miserable village. Fifty foot soldiers and nine horsemen, lead by Cabeza de Vaca, took part in the assault. No one came forth to defend the village. Inside the filthy huts, the Spaniards found only terrified women and crying children. The men had all fled into the forest. However, the fields of ripe corn and a pile of it in storage, looked as precious to the Spanish as the gold they had expected. The women were immediately put to work grinding the grain.

Within hours the Apalache men rushed out of the woods in a surprise attack. One of their arrows killed de Solís's horse. Then, as silently and suddenly as they had come, they retreated. That same day they came again, not to fight but to parlay. They demanded their women and their children. Nárvaez granted their request but kept the chieftain as a hostage.

The country surrounding the village was hilly and jungle-thick with gigantic pines, cedar, walnut, oak, laurel, and a tree called sweet gum or liquidamber, which grew profusely and gave out a heady scent. Below the hills, the marshes united numerous lakes and ponds. These, too, were impenetrable, full of thickets and fallen trees. In this green fortress the Indians waited for the invaders to go away. But they did not only wait, they made sure that the Spaniards would leave.

Years later, the American pioneers became well acquainted with the Indians' war tactics: the silent, invisible approach; the quick attack; the unexpected retreat. Such an approach was new to the Spanish, who advanced into battle in columns of four or six men, trumpets sounding, banners flying. They had no training to cope with an invisible foe that came, killed, and retreated. The arrows seemed to be shot by the branches of the trees; the screams forecasting an attack could have been those of wild birds. To pursue such an elusive enemy was useless; the Indians seemed to sink into the very earth. It was like fighting spirits, like being haunted by ghosts. Yet sometimes they were seen, and Cabeza de Vaca left a description of them.

"The Indians," he wrote, "made constant war upon us, wounding men and horses whenever they went for water. . . . All the many Indians from Florida we saw were archers, and being very tall and naked, at a distance they appear giants. These people are wonderfully built, very gaunt and of great strength and agility. Their bows are as thick as an arm, from eleven to twelve spans long, shooting an arrow at 200 paces with unerring aim. . . . Their strings are the sinews of deer. . . . If they fear an enemy, they are awake the night long, each with a bow at his side and a dozen arrows. He that would sleep tries his bow, and if it is not strung, he gives the turn necessary to the cord. They often come out from their houses, bending to the ground in such a manner that they cannot be seen, looking and watching on all sides to catch every object. If they perceive anything about, they are at once in the bushes . . . and there they remain until day. . . . When the light has come, they unbend their bows until they go out to hunt. . . . Whosoever would fight them must be cautious to show no fear, or desire to have anything that is theirs; while war exists they must be treated with the utmost rigor; for it they discover any timidity or covetousness, they are a race that well discern the opportunities for vengeance, and gather strength from any weakness of their adversaries."

When the Indians were not attacking, the men rested and talked.

"Why doesn't Nárvaez, our fearless leader, go into the woods and shoot some wild game?"

"He'd much rather eat Indian corn."

"That's why he brought us here, didn't you know? This kind of corn doesn't grow just anywhere. He's got a sweet tooth for the corn of Apalachen."

"I heard he's sent word to Cortés to come here and try some."

"I heard something else. Cabeza de Vaca is shipping the Crown its share of the native mosquitoes. Only live ones, though."

"How are they being sent?"

"By ship, of course; they wouldn't be caught dead flying through those marshlands again."

The corn the men joked about was running out. It was time for Nárvaez to make a further decision. He had sent out three scouting parties; all had gone as far as the present site of Florida's capital, Tallahassee. But the land, they reported, held no promise. The chieftain who was being held hostage, told Nárvaez, through sign language, that Apalachen was the largest of all the towns in the region. He indicated that neither North nor East nor West held any riches; that the people in all those parts were poorer than the ones in Apalachen, and even less friendly. He assured Nárvaez that he would find neither gold nor pearls there. But the South! That was the place to go. There, especially in the rich town of Aute, the natives were kind and generous. There, there was plenty of corn and beans and pumpkins. And beside that, Aute was near the sea. There was fish.

The Indian chief's main concern was to get rid of the white men. But his advice made Nárvaez happy once again. He returned to his dream. Everything might not be lost. He might yet become the governor of a wealthy land, a land that lay to the south, with a city called Aute. When they left Apalachen on July 20, after twenty-five days there, the Spaniards thought the natives would leave them alone. But on the second day, while the explorers were crossing a lake, the Indians launched an attack. The blood of both the men and the horses struck by arrows reddened the slimy water. The Spanish were held prisoner by mud and could not fight back; but even if they had been on dry land, defence would have been impossible. In the time it took a Spaniard to reload his musket, an Indian could shoot as many as seven arrows at him. Many Spaniards were wounded during that crossing, including Cabeza de Vaca; and a few were killed, among them a nobleman, Avellaneda, who was shot through the neck while helping his wounded servant.

Now, to the torture of insects, hunger, and wilderness, terror was added. The men were in constant fear of an invisible and deadly foe, against whom it was impossible to retaliate. With the men, as a perpetual reminder, were the wounded, who had to be carried; for there were too many of them for the horses to carry. The attacks came again and again; and in all of them, only two natives were killed, so elusive were they. Most of the Spaniards, even those who were not superstitious by nature, began to endow the Indians with supernatural powers. An Indian would disappear under the water of the swamp and then appear again after many minutes had passed. The Spanish were horrified.

"Only devils don't need to breathe," the men whispered to each other, unaware that the Indians did breathe, through reeds held in their mouths.

The terrible march to Aute lasted only eight days, but many of the men aged years and their hair turned white. The village, when they came to it, was neither rich nor friendly. As a matter of fact, it was non-existent. The Indians had set fire to their huts and taken to the woods. But the pumpkins, the beans, and the corn stood ripe and ready for the Spanish assault.

Nárvaez took stock. Eighteen men were dead; a dozen horses had been killed, and his dream was lost forever. If he had felt utter despair upon reaching Apalachen, here, near the smoldering remains of Aute, watching his men—all in rags, all bleeding from wounds or insect bites, all grabbing the meager crops like animals— he felt completely defeated.

Three men, Cabeza de Vaca, Andres Dorantes de Carranza, and Father Suárez, seemed to Nárvaez to be the strongest, morally and physically. They had endured in

43

silence the hardships; and they had not become, like the others, prideless in their need for food and frantic in their search for peace from the insects. And the one who seemed most like a tower of strength was Cabeza de Vaca.

Nárvaez called Cabeza de Vaca to him, for he needed to feel that strength.

"I should have taken your advice. You were right."

Nárvaez voice, usually loud and clear, was close to a whimper. Cabeza de Vaca was shocked at the sight of the conqueror of Cuba, so defeated by failure. His eye burned as if with fever, his red beard and his red hair were tangled, his clothes were dirty, his body was bent. Cabeza de Vaca felt a surge of compassion for the man but could not bear to look at him, could not bear to hear him apologize.

"What would you have me do?" Cabeza de Vaca asked.

"I beg you," Nárvaez said, aware of using the verb for the first time in his life to one not his superior, "to go and look for the sea. We must find our ships. We must go back, or we shall all die here in this desolate land."

"I will go at once."

"Take Dorantes with you. He is a good man. And be careful, for I need you."

With Dorantes went his Negro slave, Estebanico. This giant of a man had come from the coast of Morocco and had served his master faithfully in Spain. Unlike the rest of the men in Nárvaez' expedition, the Florida wilderness held no terror for him. He was the only one who looked with great curiosity on the Indians, if not at the men, then certainly at the girls and women. When others walked, he was likely to run; when others stumbled, he helped them; when others mumbled, he sang; and when the rest swore, he laughed.

Fifty foot soldiers and seven horsemen set off with these three, in search of the sea and the ships. Reaching the Gulf of Mexico, the men found great oyster beds. It was a gift from the sea; they stayed near the beds overnight. The following day they explored the coast. There were many inlets and countless bays, but the open sea was impossible to reach by land. Cabeza de Vaca was soon convinced that the only way the expedition could ever leave the coastal marshes was by small boats. These boats they would have to build themselves.

It was with this recommendation that he hurried back to Aute. He found near disaster there. The Indians had attacked again, another one of the horses had been killed, and several soldiers had been wounded. But most of the men had not even been aware of the attack. Malaria was rife among them. Those afflicted with the fever lay on the ground, helpless and delirious.

To stay on at Aute was unwise; for another attack would wipe them out. However, to set off seemed impossible; most of the men could not move. But the instinct for survival has great power. The march towards the sea began the following morning. The destination was the oyster beds, where at least there would be food. And from there, they could see water, even if it was not the open sea. Maybe the ships were sailing up the coast looking for them, maybe . . .

Broiling under the sun, bitten by clouds of swarming insects, the men staggered on. Many of them mumbled incoherently and shook with fever.

"The journey was extremely difficult, for neither did we have enough horses to carry the sick, nor did we know what remedy to give them, and more were falling sick every day, and it was a matter of great grief and pain to see the hardship and need in which we were. When we had arrived, we saw how little use there was in going further, for there was no place to go; and even if there had been, our men could not have gone forward, for most of them were sick and in such state that there was little they could do."

When they reached the Gulf of Mexico again, at what is now the Bay of St. Marks, it seemed to those who were capable of coherent thought that they had come to their final resting place.

Under cover of darkness and away from the mutterings of the sick, two dozen men planned to escape death.

"The only way out of here is to ride out."

"The horses can save us."

"There are twenty-four of them still alive. One for each of us."

"We'll reach Tampa Bay and the ships that are waiting there."

"But how about the others? How about the sick?"

"They are all dying."

"To stay with them would be suicide."

"If I did not believe that they are doomed, I would not think of leaving the others."

"Our duty is to save ourselves and get word to the ships. It's the only way.

Cabeza de Vaca, who with Dorantes and Father

Suárez was making a tour of the camp, overheard the plan. "We showed them," he wrote later, "the deformity of their purpose. . . . They determined to remain, and that whatever might happen to one should be the lot of all, without any forsaking the rest." The three men must have used exceptional persuasion to stop the desertion.

Nárvaez, notified of the planned escape, not only readily forgave the would-be-traitors, but humbly asked his men for advice. The decision they reached was the same as Cabeza de Vaca's: the only way out was by water. They would have to build boats.

"We commenced to build on the 4th of August, with only one carpenter in the company, and we proceeded with so great a diligence that on the 20th of September, five boats were finished, 33 feet in length, each caulked with the fiber of the palmetto. We pitched them with a certain resin, made from pine trees by a Greek, named Don Theodoro, from the same husk of the palmetto; and from the tails and manes of the horses we made ropes and rigging, from our shirts, sails; and from the junipers growing there we made the oars that appeared to us requisite. Such was the country into which our sins had cast us, that only by very great search could we find stone for ballast and anchors, since in it all we had not seen one. We flayed the horses, taking the skin from their legs entire, and tanning them to make canteens wherein to carry water."

Thus, despair gave birth to ingenuity. The men's will to survive was amazing. They raided Aute for corn and amassed six hundred bushels of it. They lived on oysters, corn, horsemeat, wild game, and fish. They were men driven. Their only thought was to escape

47

alive. During those weeks, ten more men were killed by Indians; the arrows pierced their heavy armor.

"Before we embarked, there died more than forty men of disease and hunger, without enumerating those destroyed by the Indians. By the 22nd of the month of September, the horses had been consumed, one only remaining." Cabeza de Vaca adds that he could never bring himself to eat horsemeat. He does not give a reason for this, but it is probable that he loved the brave, long suffering animals so much that he could not bear to think of eating them.

"After the provisions and clothes had been taken in, not over half a foot of the gunwale remained above water; and more than this, the boats were so crowded that we could not move—so much can necessity do, which drove us to hazard our lives in this manner, running into a turbulent sea, not a single one who went having a knowledge of navigation."

As the survivors, 247 Spaniards, raised their shirt-sails, they prayed that their poor crafts would carry them to the nearest Spanish settlement in Mexico, Pánuco. They were so ignorant of the geography of the area that they did not know that Pánuco was six times further away than Tampa Bay, where their ships stood at anchor waiting for them. Hope, not knowledge, carried them on.

In the bay the shallows and reefs held them prisoner for several days, the crafts moving in and out of sand bars. Finally strong winds helped them escape the shallows, and they could look back on the bay, which they called the Bay of Horses, and shudder with memories of their six months in Florida.

5

The boats, made more with ingenuity than dexterity, kept inexplicably afloat. But that did not solve all of the expedition's problems.

The first disaster to overtake the men was lack of water. The containers made of horse leg hides rotted and spoiled the water inside. Since a third of the men still suffered from fever, their thirst seemed unendurable.

A week after they had set off, Cabeza de Vaca's boat sighted five Indian canoes. The natives, terrified by the appearance of the eerie crafts, dove into the water and swam to a nearby island. The men went ashore and found a small Indian village with some food in it. Cabeza de Vaca took the abandoned canoes, secured them to the sides of the Spanish boats, and thus raised his gunwales

16 inches above the water.

The boats wandered in and out of the bays and inlets of North Florida in search of food and water. By the middle of October, they had reached Santa Rosa Island, a bare strip of beach. There a fierce storm overtook them. "We remained there for six days without venturing to leave, and it being five days since we had drunk anything, our thirst was so great as to compel us to drink salt water, and several of us took such an excess of it that we lost suddenly five men."

The seas were high and the skies still angry when they decided to set sail again. It seemed far better to drown than to go mad for want of water. That very afternoon they reached the placid waters of the present Pensacola Bay. Here the miracle of their staying afloat on the heavy seas was followed by another cause for rejoicing. Several canoes met them, and the natives made welcoming signs. The boats dropped anchor. Staggering out unto the land, the Spaniards threw themselves at the pots of fresh water that stood in front of each native hut. The chief ordered cooked seafood brought to the white men. In an atmosphere of mutual trust and friendship, gifts were exchanged. That night, for the first time in weeks, the Spaniards went to sleep without fear, their stomachs full, their thirst appeased. Cabeza de Vaca, Nárvaez, and a handful of others had been invited to spend the night in the chief's house; the other men, too exhausted to move, fell asleep on the beach.

They had slept only a few hours, when, without warning, they found themselves being attacked. The sleeping men were beaten with fists and with stones; those who attempted to flee were pursued by arrows.

Nárvaez, bleeding from the face, would have been killed had it not been for Cabeza de Vaca and a few others who came to his rescue. There seemed to be no plan to the attack, and certainly the Spanish presented no organized defense. In the darkness they all fought as best they could, but the dazed and weakened Spaniards would have been all killed had it not been for the quick thinking of Dorantes. With fifteen soldiers he crept away from the village and attacked it from the rear. This action so confused and frightened the Indians that they fled. Only three among the Spanish had been killed, but, "not one of us escaped unhurt. I was wounded in the face; and if they had had more arrows, without any doubt they would have done us great harm."

Because a strong north wind was blowing, making the sea extremely dangerous, the Spaniards decided to stay a while and risk another attack rather than return to their unstable boats. To keep warm, they chopped up the Indian canoes for firewood. The Indians did not return, and when, in the afternoon, the wind died somewhat, the Spanish boarded their boats once again, taking with them clay jars filled with fresh water and whatever food they were able to find in the village.

They sailed for another four days, until once more they ran out of drinking water. Had they chosen to go in the opposite direction, when they first set out, they might now have reached Tampa Bay and the ships that waited there for them. Instead they came to what is now Mobile Bay, where an Indian canoe met them. The natives in the canoe nodded their heads when a request for water was made. Theodoro, the carpenter chiefly responsible for the building of the boats, together with a

Negro, boarded the canoe with the precious clay jars. As soon as they touched land, the two men decided to desert. They had had enough of the horrible life at sea; it seemed better to take their chances with the seemingly hospitable Indians. The canoe drifted back to the expedition, the jars unfilled. The Spanish at once assumed that the Indians had made captives of the men and sailed in to demand their return. No one, not even Cabeza de Vaca, believed the natives, who came out in a canoe, when they indicated that the two men had chosen to stay of their own free will. Cabeza de Vaca ordered the capture of two hostages. The chief of the village tried to negotiate for the return of the hostages, but Nárvaez remained firm. He would have his men back, or the hostages would be retained. This angered the natives, who felt they had no choice but to attack.

For the first time since the journey began, the Spaniards faced slingshots. A large number of canoes encircled the boats, the Indians raining stones and rocks on the Spaniards, who could not take cover. Desperately the men fought to maneuver their awkward crafts out of reach of the weapons, but the only escape was the open sea. Cabeza de Vaca wrote that the men were "sorrowful and much dejected" at leaving behind two of their comrades. Eleven years later, Hernando de Soto's soldiers were shown a dagger that had belonged to Theodoro. But his fate and that of the Negro, who preferred uncertainty on land to death at sea, remained a mystery.

A few days later, propelled by a strong wind, the boats entered one of the mouths of the Mississippi River. Although de Soto is credited with its discovery, it was Nárvaez who first saw its gigantic estuary.

It was the river's strong current that was responsible for the next tragedy. Struggling to reach land against the tide, the boats became separated. Four days later, on November 1st, Cabeza de Vaca's boat sighted the one in which Nárvaez rode and another, which was too far off to identify.

"Where are the others?" Cabeza de Vaca shouted to Nárvaez when the two boats came close.

"I don't know," Nárvaez shouted back. "Maybe they drifted to land. What would you have us do?"

"We must join the one boat we see. They might have news of the others. And we must join it immediately."

Nárvaez consulted his colleague, Captain Pantoja.

"It's too far away; we can never hope to catch up with it," he shouted. "We can't spare the time. If we don't reach land today, we'll drift out to sea and bypass Pánuco."

"But we must try! We can't give up without trying!" Cabeza de Vaca was angry. Since the beginning of the expedition he had felt that their strength and hope of success lay in keeping together. Nárvaez tended to dissipate that strength.

There was no answer from Nárvaez. Cabeza de Vaca saw him give orders to proceed in the direction in which he believed the land must lie.

"Discovering his will, I took my oar, and so did everyone his, in my boat. We rowed until near sunset. . . . It being winter and the cold very great, and as we had been suffering so many days from hunger and from the injuries we received from the waves, that the next day people began to break down, so that when the sun set all those aboard of my barge had fallen in a heap and were so near dying that few remained conscious, and not five men kept on their feet. When the night came, the skipper and I were the only ones able to manage the barge."

Since Nárvaez' boat was by far the largest and had the most able men aboard, Cabeza de Vaca, in his desperation, called out for help.

"You must throw us a line," he shouted. "It will be dark soon, and we'll lose each other forever."

"Impossible!" Nárvaez called back. "We can barely manage to keep rowing ourselves."

"What would you have us do then?"

"From now on, it's each man for himself. That is my last order to you."

Cabeza de Vaca watched the governor's boat disappear into the dark with anger and a heavy heart. Alone there seemed to be no chance for survival.

Hope did not return until another boat, captained by Peñalosa and Téllez, drew near. For the next four days and nights, these two boats sailed side by side, pushed by strong winds. Their course took them away from land and into ever colder weather and high seas. Then the merely bad weather changed into a storm, and the two boats became separated. By this time Cabeza de Vaca was the only one in his boat still on his feet; the other men "were fallen one on another, so near to death that there were few among them in a state of sensibility . . ." For the first time in his life, Cabeza de Vaca preferred death to life.

On the morning of the 6th of November, 1528, the exhausted, starving men heard the thundering sound of breaking surf. They were approaching some land. The waves that carried them to shore were so high and powerful that their boat was lifted up and thrown down onto the beach with great force. The men spilled out of it, falling like rag dolls into the boiling surf. They crawled as best as they could, blinded by the salt water, gasping for breath, half-drowned, to the safety of a sand dune. Most of them were too dazed to know if they were dead or alive.

They had been sailing for forty-six days, and their incredibly crude craft had covered close to a thousand miles of the Gulf of Mexico. In all probability the waves washed them ashore on Galveston Island, in what is now Texas. In his narrative Cabeza de Vaca refers to the island as Mal Hado, the Island of Bad Luck.

Beyond the sand dunes stood small pools of rain water. The men crawled to them on their knees. Still crawling, they gathered driftwood for a fire, which they needed if they were not to freeze in the cold wind. A few handfuls of corn, saved from the wreck, were warmed over the fire and eaten gratefully.

Cabeza de Vaca asked Lope de Oviedo, the only other man among them capable of standing on his feet, to see what kind of a place they had come to. Climbing a tree, Oviedo reported that they were on an island and that he saw a path, which he volunteered to explore. He walked until he found a village of Indian huts, deserted except for a small dog. This he scooped up in his hands to carry back to the men. Before he reached the beach, three Indians appeared and barred his way. Oviedo calmly motioned for them to follow him. Soon many other natives came out of the forest to observe, silently, the strange human wreckage on the beach. "If they were not large, our fears made giants of them." But this time the Spaniards need not have feared.

Cabeza de Vaca had been able to salvage some beads and hawk bells when he was thrown into the water, and now he distributed these as peace offerings. Several of the natives immediately surrendered to him their arrows, as a sign of friendship and trust, and informed him that they would provide food in the morning. At sunrise they came —a long procession of men, women and children—bearing gifts of fish and roots and precious water.

Well-fed and rested, the Spaniards attempted to patch up their boat, which had been grounded and badly battered by the waves. After a while the natives left, unable to bear the sight of such wearying labors. The job done, after a fashion, the entire crew of the boat managed to climb on board just seconds before a giant wave hit. The boat went down in the boiling foam; the oars were swept under and so were the men. De Solís and two other men were drowned as the craft sank out of sight. The rest of the men managed to get to the beach.

"It pleased Our Lord that reaching the remnants of our fires we found wood with which we built big fires and then with many tears begged Our Lord for mercy and forgiveness for our sins. Every one of us pitied not only himself, but all the others whom he saw in the same condition. At sunset the Indians, thinking we had not left, came to bring us food. . . . Upon seeing the disaster we had suffered, our misery and distress, the Indians sat down with us and all began to weep out of compassion for our misfortune, and for more than half an hour they wept so loudly and so sincerely that it could be heard far away. Verily, to see beings so devoid of reason, untutored, so like unto brutes, yet so deeply moved by pity for us, it increased my feelings and those of others in my company for our own misfortune." And the Spanish joined in the general weeping.

The generous behavior of the natives convinced Cabeza de Vaca that they could be fully trusted. Since his men were all exhausted and most of them were too ill to remain on the cold, windy shore, he asked the Indians if they would accept the men into their huts. The Indians were delighted with the idea and were most eager to get the Spaniards into their village.

"Against the cold, and lest on the way some one of us might faint or die, they had provided four or five big fires on the road, at each one of which they warmed us. As soon as they saw we had regained a little warmth and strength, they would carry us to the next fire with such haste that our feet barely touched the ground."

This great show of kindness and hospitality made the Spaniards suspicious. The natives' thoughtfulness was boundless, and their eagerness to make the Spaniards comfortable amazing. Why were they so kind? The men began to murmur among themselves:

"They'll sacrifice us!"

"That's exactly what I've been thinking!"

"We don't have anything of value, so they won't kill us because they want to rob us . . ."

"They're cannibals, and that's enough reason for them to kill us."

"I'm not sure about that. About their being cannibals. I only meant that they will kill us and offer us as sacrifices to their gods."

"Will they torture us first?"

"But they are kind and generous . . ."

"And savages. You never know with savages."

Even Cabeza de Vaca grew uneasy when they reached the village.

"About one hour after our arrival they began to dance and to make a great celebration (which lasted the whole night), although there was neither pleasure, feast nor sleep in it for us, since we expected to be sacrificed. In the morning they gave us fish and roots, and treated us so well that we became reassured, losing somewhat our apprehension of being butchered."

The next day Cabeza de Vaca and his men were surprised and delighted to learn that another boat, the one captained by Dorantes and Castillo, had been marooned on the other side of the island and that their fellow countrymen were not far away. A reunion took place with great jubilation.

It was agreed that some of the men would board Dorantes' undamaged boat and try reaching Pánuco by sea. The rest would wait on the island for help to come. But again bad luck pursued the castaways. No sooner had the boat been launched than it foundered and sank.

They were now truly stranded. Their journey by sea had come to an end.

Four Spaniards volunteered to swim to the mainland and find a route to Mexico. They were among the few who knew how to swim and the few who were well enough to try. The others, eighty men in all, would have to wait for help to come. If necessary, they would spend the entire winter among the friendly Indians. So as not to put too great a burden on the natives and their meager supply of food, the Spaniards separated and went to live in different villages. The island was inhabited by two tribes, the Capoques and the Hans. They had similar customs and were friendly with each other. Cabeza de Vaca left a thorough description of them.

"Of all the people in the world, they are those who most love their children and treat them best, and should the child of one of them happen to die, the parents and relatives bewail it, and the whole settlement, the lament lasting a full year, day after day. Before sunrise the parents begin to weep, after them the tribe, and the same they do at noon and at dawn. At the end of the year of mourning, they celebrate the anniversary and wash and cleanse themselves of all their paint. They mourn all their dead in this manner, old people excepted, to whom they do not pay any attention, saying that these have had their time and are no longer of any use, but only take space, and food from the children.

"They have the custom, when they know each other and meet from time to time, before they speak, to weep for half an hour. After they have wept the one who receives the visit rises and gives to the other all he has. The other takes it, and in a little while goes away with everything. Even sometimes, after having given and obtained all, they part without having uttered a word.

"They have no other arms than bows and arrows, in the use of which they are very dexterous. The men have one of their nipples bored from side to side, and some have both, wearing a cane in each, the length of two palms and a half, and the thickness of two fingers. They have the under lip also bored, and wear in it a piece of cane the breadth of half a finger. Their women are accustomed to great toil. . . . Every man has an acknowledged wife. The physicians are allowed more freedom: they may have two or three wives, among whom exist the greatest friendship and harmony.

"There is great want of wood; mosquitoes are in great plenty. The houses are of mats, set up on masses of oyster shells, which they sleep upon, and in skins, should they accidentally possess them.

"They have no chief. All that are of a lineage keep together."

The days that Cabeza de Vaca and his men spent among these people stretched into weeks, and the weeks into months. The winter became extremely cruel. Raging winds and chilling cold prevented the men from fishing and gathering roots. Famine began. The Indians endured hunger stoically, but the Spaniards seemed to go mad from it. ". . . Five Christians quartered on the coast were driven to such an extremity that they ate each other up until but one remained, who being left alone, there was nobody to eat him. . . . At this the Indians were so startled, and there was such an uproar among them, that I verily believe if they had seen this at the beginning they would have killed them, and we all would have been in great danger."

But hunger was not the chief killer that dreadful winter. A terrible disease struck all those on the island, a wildfire epidemic, that wiped out more than half of the native population and took an even greater toll of Spaniards. By early January, 1529, only fifteen were alive, among them Cabeza de Vaca, Dorantes, Castillo, the notary Lope de Oviedo, and the Negro, Estebanico.

These few survivors had next to cope with something more dangerous than illness and famine. They had to cope with hatred. The natives turned against them. The Indians blamed the Spaniards for the illness that had taken so many lives, imagining them capable of a great and evil power. If it had not been for the Indian in whose house Cabeza de Vaca was living, all fifteen would have been killed. Cabeza de Vaca convinced his host that the Spaniards did not possess any power, good or evil. If they had any such power, he argued why would they have allowed so many of their own to die? The plea was a convincing one. Perhaps it was even too convincing. For the natives began to think of Cabeza de Vaca as an extraordinarily wise man, much wiser even than their own physicians. Their medicine men had died in the epidemic, and the natives were restless without supernatural protection. "They wished to make us physicians without examination or inquiring for diplomas." It did no good to protest that they could perform no cures, that they knew nothing of medicine, the Indians insisted. And finally their threats, or possibly the pity the white men felt for their ignorant hosts, won through; Cabeza de Vaca became the head of a group of white witch doctors.

"The way we treated the sick was to make over them the sign of the cross while breathing on them, re-cite a Pater Noster and Ave Maria, and pray to God, Our Lord, as best we could to give them good health and inspire them to do us some favors. Thanks to His will and the mercy He had upon us, all those for whom we prayed, as soon as we crossed them, told the others that they were cured and felt well again. For this they gave us good cheer, and would rather be without food themselves so as to give it to us, and they gave us hides and other small things. So great was the lack of food then that I often remained without eating anything whatsoever for three days, and they were in the same plight, so that it seemed to me impossible for life to last."

Hunger finally drove the Indians to seek food on the mainland. Dorantes, Castillo, and several others accompanied the Hans tribe across the bay to oyster beds on the shore of the Texas mainland. The Capoques took Cabeza de Vaca with them shortly afterwards. They fished for mackerel, flounder, sheep's head, jew-fish, red fish, and sea-trout. The Indians stood in water up to their hips, each with a bow ready, and shot the fish with arrows. Their aim was marvellous, and they found this way superior to any other way of catching fish. But throughout his odyssey, Cabeza de Vaca, even in midst of famine, had difficulty in swallowing seafood. His dislike of it equalled the revulsion he felt for horsemeat. Now, perhaps from the seafood or perhaps from some other cause, he fell ill and soon seemed close to death.

The news of his illness reached his friends, who with the coming of warm spring weather had decided it was time to search inland for Pánuco. Thirteen Spaniards started off, without even seeing Cabeza de Vaca because they were told he was dying. He was left alone with the Indians. He did not die, but during his illness, his hosts lost all faith in his power as a physician. Seeing him so sick for such a long time, they began to treat him badly; and when he recovered, he found himself their slave.

6

Cabeza de Vaca's descent to slavery from his lofty position as witch doctor was sudden and steep. After his illness, the Indians gave him the most menial tasks, tasks they themselves were unwilling to perform. His life was worse than that of a dog for whom no one cares. There was no end to his labors. His duties included: gathering wood for the fires; digging under water and under the earth for roots, the staple food of the natives; catching fish and game; cleaning around the camp; carrying heavy loads. "From this employment I had my fingers so tender that at but a straw's touch they would bleed."

With back bent, hands blistered, body punished by hunger and the weather, skin leperous from mosquito bites, the grey-haired man, "the Treasurer of His Majesty the Emperor Charles V . . . had descended from his pride to the most abject state of any human creature. He who had turned away from the flesh of the horses would now fall gratefully upon a rat or a lizard. There was no ease for his body anywhere, and no flickering of cheer for his mind save in the hope of death . . . He never questioned his God's purpose nor doubted divine goodness. Chopping at the stubborn roots with his wooden hoe, he praised God for his mysterious bounty. Into his soul, purged of all pride and of every evil growth that feeds on spiritual ease, came God's gift of courage." [1]

For a whole year there was no opportunity to even attempt an escape. Still on the mainland, he waited patiently for his masters to return to the Island of Bad Luck, where he expected to be reunited with his fellow Spaniards. When they finally did return to the island, he discovered to his horror that only one of them was still there. He was Lope de Oviedo, or what was left of Lope de Oviedo, for he had become so thin and weak he was barely recognizable. Even more terrifying than his appearance, however, was his single-mindedness.

"Did you bring me anything to eat? What did you eat on the mainland? Why didn't you bring me anything? Why didn't you think of it? I know you have food, why are you hiding it from me? Is it because you want to surprise me?" His huge eyes in a skull-like face looked imploringly or shifted uneasily with fright.

Only after long questioning, and then with great indifference, did Oviedo tell Cabeza de Vaca that the

[1] Morris Bishop, *The Odyssey of Cabeza de Vaca*, Century, N. Y., 1933

64

others had all left. He didn't know how long before—a year, two, what did it matter, how was he expected to know? By now, Cabeza de Vaca realized, the men could be in Mexico. But this would do him little good, for they probably believed him dead. Could one man make the trip alone? Or two? He began to talk to Oviedo of escape. But Oviedo would not hear of it. He was afraid to take a chance: he wanted to be left in peace; he could not swim and would drown; there would be no food and he would die of hunger. "I want to live!" Oviedo shouted; and Cabeza de Vaca wept at the shout. For life reduced to such debasement of spirit was not life.

For him there was no choice but to escape alone, to find a way to Mexico, and to come back for Oviedo. For Cabeza de Vaca had no thought but to save him. He could not bear to see him so preoccupied with his meager food, so content with the warmth of the sun, so ready to vegetate until death.

During the time Cabeza de Vaca had spent on the mainland, he had met a friendly tribe of Indians, the Charrucos. He now decided to escape to them, bringing with him seashells, which they used as knives. They were precious and rare there, and he was sure he could trade them for food and for information about his friends and the way to Pánuco.

His plans worked well, better than he had anticipated. And soon he was moving from camp to camp on the mainland, trading and gathering information.

"Trading along with my wares, I penetrated inland as far as I cared to go and along the coast as much as forty or fifty leagues. My stock consisted mainly of pieces of seashells and cockles, and shells with which

65

they cut a fruit which is like a bean, used by them for healing and in their dances and feasts. This is of greatest value among them, besides shell beads and other objects. These things I carried inland, and in exchange brought back hides; red ochre, with which they rub and dye their faces and hair; flint for arrow points; . . . and tassels made of the hair of deer, which they dye red. This trade suited me well because it gave me the liberty to go wherever I pleased; I was not bound to do anything and no longer a slave. . . . I became well-known among them (the Charrucos); they rejoiced greatly when seeing me and I would bring them what they needed, and those who did not know me would desire and endeavor to meet me for the sake of my fame."

His fame was indeed considerable and for good reasons: he was a white man, a traveling salesman among people who knew neither white men nor traders; he was a great curiosity. Wherever he went, Indians greeted him as a friend, by rubbing their hands first on their own chests and then on his. They would argue, after this greeting, most heatedly over the value of his wares, bargaining at length, either in sign language or in their own tongue, which sounded to him like the clucking of hens. He was accepted into their huts, where with them he drank a bitter black brew made with yaupon leaves. This beverage was prepared with great care and ceremony and consumed in quantities as large as six gallons a day per man. All who drank of it were made ill, but this did not prevent the brew from being very popular.

Cabeza de Vaca got to know his customers well, including their feuds and their customs. They fought frequently among themselves, sometimes using bows and arrows but more often using bare knuckles. Only women were allowed to part fighters; the men never interfered. After a fight, the participants would go away to cool their tempers, and return bearing gifts, their anger forgotten. During tribal warfare the men would sleep with their bows ready. They would build their camp at the edge of the woods, dig trenches around it, and lure their enemies with fires. The foes would fall into the trenches like trapped animals.

Among these people Cabeza de Vaca never feared, and that lack of fear made his existence a happy one. He learned their dances and their songs; he learned to love their children and play with them. And during wintertime, when life itself seemed to be hibernating, he rested among them and suffered with them from the weather and from the hunger.

For several years this pattern of life continued. Each spring he went back to Oviedo, trying to get him to leave. Cabeza de Vaca was certain that both of them could make it safely to Mexico. He had paved the way for them with good will. But each spring Oviedo refused, promising that the next spring he would go. Each spring they parted angrily, after bitter quarreling, Cabeza de Vaca's pity for the man having turned to impatience and disgust. Yet he could not bear to abandon his cowardly friend. So each year he returned to the mainland to spend yet another year with the Indians.

In 1532, when he came to Oviedo in the spring, Cabeza de Vaca refused to leave the island without him. It was summer before he broke Oviedo's resistance, and they set off. They crossed to the mainland by canoe. There they walked along well traveled paths, paths

67

Cabeza de Vaca knew better now, than those of his own native country. The first barrier they came to was Oyster Creek. Here Oviedo refused to go any further. He could not swim, he would drown. But his friend, now considered more of a tormenter than a savior, ordered him to cling to his shoulders. Cabeza de Vaca swam across the creek with his friend, a protesting burden, on his back. Together with a group of Doguenes Indians, the two crossed the Brazos River on a raft. Beyond lay a land inhabited by Indians they did not know.

These Indians were the Quevenes; and he found that although he had never traded among them, they had heard of him. They informed the two arrivals that in the vicinity, among the Mariames Indians, were two more white men and a giant Negro. Cabeza de Vaca's joy at hearing this was marred by further information. His countrymen were being cruelly treated. To show how cruelly, the Quevenes, laughing loudly, began to beat Oviedo and Cabeza de Vaca. They hit them with sticks, threw mud at them, pinched them, and to frighten them even further, poised arrows at their hearts.

Lope de Oviedo wept with terror. He had left his peaceful island to deliver himself to madmen, bent on killing him for a joke. When some women set off in the direction of Bad Luck Island, he went with them, deaf to Cabeza de Vaca's pleas.

As his friend disappeared, Cabeza de Vaca felt more anger than grief. He had wasted almost three years, trying to save the man from his own cowardice. He had done his duty; there was no need for him to wait longer.

7

Once again Cabeza de Vaca was alone among an unfriendly people. But just as so many times before, bad luck brought good. One of the Doguenes Indians who had come across the Brazos with him agreed to bring Cabeza de Vaca together with a fellow Spaniard.

It was Dorantes whom he saw first. The two were joined shortly after by Castillo and Estebanico. "We gave many thanks at seeing ourselves together, and this was a day to us of the greatest pleasure we had enjoyed in life." The reunion was tearful and highly emotional. The sight of three white men, bearded and naked, and a black man, decorated still with trinkets, crying and shouting in an incomprehensible tongue, amused the Indians enough to send them into gales of laughter.

The men had not seen each other for four years. Cabeza de Vaca, the others had believed dead. They had also learned from an encounter with two other men from the expedition, Figueroa and Esquivel, that the boat with Nárvaez had been swept out to sea, with all aboard presumably killed. In fact, all boats, except that captained by Peñalosa and Téllez, were known to be lost. And of all the men who had left the Island of Bad Luck, only these three had survived.

During their short reunion the four men talked about escape but decided to wait for six months before attempting it. At that time the Indians would be going southwest for prickly pears. It would be a time of general gluttony, and the Mariames would be unlikely to take time out to hunt down their slaves.

Castillo was sent to live with the Iguaces, a neighboring tribe; and Dorantes and Cabeza de Vaca were held together in the household of a family afflicted with blindness in one eye. Estebanico was a slave in another household.

Cabeza de Vaca, in his journal, described their masters, the Mariames, a people only slightly removed from the Stone Age:

"In obedience to their customs, they take life, destroying even their children on account of dreams. They cast away their daughters at birth, and cause them to be eaten by dogs. . . . When the men would marry, they buy the women of their enemies: the price paid for a wife is a bow, the best that can be got, with two arrows . . . or a net a fathom in length and another in breath. . . . The women work very hard, and do a great deal: of the twenty-four hours they have only six of repose; the rest of the night they pass in heating the ovens to bake . . . roots to eat. At daybreak they begin to dig them, to bring wood and water to their houses and get in readiness for other things that may be necessary."

Besides roots, which constituted the chief food of the Mariames, "they eat earth and wood and all that there is, the dung of deer and other things that I omit to mention. And I honestly believe that were there stones in that land, they would eat them. . . . It occurred to us many times while we were among this people and there was no food, to be three or four days without eating, when they, to revive our spirits, would tell us not to be sad, that soon there would be prickly pears when we would eat plenty and drink of the juice, when our bellies would be very big and we should be content and joyful."

Cabeza de Vaca was filled with admiration for the stamina of the Mariames: "These Indians are so accustomed to running, that without rest or fatigue they follow a deer from morning to night." The deer would collapse from exhaustion, and the natives would catch it with their bare hands; or the animal, terrified by the endless pursuit, would run in its panic into the sea and drown. A feast on deer meat would be followed by dances and festivities, the Mariames being a merry people in spite of their cruelty.

The mosquitoes in that part of Texas were as merciless as those in Florida. "From my own experience, I can state there is no torment known in this world that can equal it." The Indians burned wet wood, to make a protective smoke screen, but the smoke made the men as uncomfortable as the bites of the insects. ". . . we did little else than shed tears from the smoke that came

71

into our eyes, besides feeling intense heat from the many fires."

The Spaniards, together with the Indians, lived for the season of the prickly pear—the end of hunger and also, for the Spanish, the time of escape. The days passed slowly in slavery. If it had not been for the companionship of Dorantes, Cabeza de Vaca would have tried fleeing earlier. But the two were together, and being together made up for many things.

The two spent many sleepless nights, remembering their lives in Spain, crying over the lost dream of conquering Florida, and singing their native songs, the mournful *cante hondo*, the Moorish lament.

They also planned their escape. And now it was not to Mexico that they planned to go. Reports on the American bison were responsible for this change. They had heard that the animals "come as far as the seacoast of Texas from a northerly direction, ranging through tract of more than four hundred leagues; and throughout the whole region over which they had run, the people who inhabit near, descend and live upon them, distributing a vast many hides into the interior country . . ." The unknown continent expanded for them. It was larger and stretched much farther north than they had suspected. It was, as Cabeza de Vaca had once suggested to Nárvaez, a whole continent, one that might possibly stretch as far as India and Japan. If they could explore it, they might change the map of the world as much as Christopher Columbus had. To do so would render greater service to humanity and to Spain than would just escaping. And so they had made a decision—they would go north and west. "We chose this course because in traversing the country we should learn many particulars of it, so that should God, Our Lord be pleased to take any of us thence, and lead us to the land of the Christians, we might carry that information and news of it."

The trek towards the pear harvest was a long one, some seventy-five miles. Many tribes, including of course the Mariames and the Iguaces, traveled up the San Antonio River at that time, for the same purpose. In the fall of 1533 all four survivors of the Nárvaez expedition met on the trail and set the time and place for their escape.

During the time of the ripe pears, while the many tribes were together, tribal wars were forgotten. All talked and made merry. It was there that the Spaniards learned the fate of the only craft unaccounted for, the one captained by Peñalosa and Téllez. Some of the Indians proudly showed them what little remained of the shipwrecked crew: garments, knives, and pieces of armor. The four mourned their friends and companions, knowing that now they, and possibly Oviedo, were the only ones who remained. With this awareness came a sudden feeling that for some great and as yet unrevealed reason God had chosen to spare them. This conviction persisted in them, filling them with faith and courage and a sense of wonder.

All went well with their plans until the night before their planned escape. Then a Mariame warrior got into a fight with an Iguace, and the tribes separated in anger. This took Castillo away, and there could be no escape for any, unless they all could go. When the prickly pear season ended, they were slaves still.

A dreadful year followed. From September of 1533 until the summer of 1534 there was so much toil, so much hunger, and so much physical discomfort that Cabeza de Vaca could hardly bear to recall it; he wrote about it only briefly: "During that time I fared very badly, as well from lack of food as from the abuse the Indians gave me. So badly was I treated that I had to flee three times from my masters, and they all went in my pursuit ready to kill me. But God, Our Lord, in His infinite goodness, protected and saved my life."

The one-eyed master died, and Dorantes was separated from Cabeza de Vaca. Neither knew of Castillo's or Estebanico's fate.

When the prickly pear season came again and the trek inland began, Cabeza de Vaca knew that he could not endure another year of slavery. But death was not the alternative he wanted. He was determined that all four of them should make a successful escape.

All four men were at least alive, and all arrived at the prickly pear harvest. They met, and once again designated a place and a time of escape. It was to be the night of September 21. Cabeza de Vaca, Dorantes, and Estebanico managed to escape first. Castillo, who was by now with a tribe of Lanegados, joined them the next day.

Together at last, the four faced a new life: a life of free men. Their path was uncharted, their future uncertain, their plans vague. They knew only that the future could not be worse than the past.

8

His companions chose Cabeza de Vaca as their leader. They all acknowledged his bravery, superior intellect, resourcefulness, and determination. His deep faith in God, his trust in the triumph of honesty and justice, inspired them. During his slavery, he had lost none of his dignity. His carriage was still that of a gentleman, though his body was barely covered and his skin was rough and almost black. In stature he was the smallest of the four.

Castillo, the tallest of the Christians, was an aristocrat from Salamanca, a doctor's son. His life, however, had never been that of a gentleman of leisure. He had always been an adventurer and a gambler. His captain's rank had been awarded him in battle; and his bravery under fire, had won him his spurs.

Dorantes, a native of Béjar, was proud of both sides of his family. Both his mother and his father were descendents of old and noble families. He, too, was a captain, decorated for bravery in battle. More quiet and more serious than Castillo, his courage was limitless and his craving for adventure never satisfied. He was an extraordinarily strong man, although neither big nor very tall.

His slave, Estebanico, was, more than the others, possessed of the qualities of a pioneer: defiance, a friendly nature, fearlessness, the curiosity of a cat, the brute strength of a bull, and the disposition of an optimist. Estebanico was not a Christian.

These four made their way cautiously at first, imagining that their masters were pursuing them. The country they were crossing was one of cacti, low bushes, and unknown Indians. They did not know what to expect, and certainly they did not anticipate eager friendship. But the news of their prowess as healers had come from the Island of Bad Luck to the Avavares, the first people they met. The news, recently arrived, was some four years late. The downfall of the Spanish and their recent slavery was not known.

When the four reached the first Avavare camp, they fully expected a hostile reception; instead they were welcomed joyfully. Cabeza de Vaca failed to convince the Indians that the four no longer practiced medicine. Medicine men did not resign nor retire.

It was to Castillo, that the Indians turned first. The day the Spanish arrived, several of the tribesmen came to him complaining of headaches. He followed the same procedure they had used four years before, and the

Indians proclaimed their cure after Castillo's ministrations.

As they fell asleep that night, the four shivered with an uneasy feeling. This forced return to the precarious profession that had once led to slavery was not of their choice. They knew that the Indians understood only success and would never forgive failure.

"Early the next day many Indians came and brought five people who were paralyzed and very ill, and they came for Castillo to cure them. Every one of the patients offered him his bow and arrows, which he accepted, and by sunset he had made the sign of the cross over each of the sick, recommending them to God, Our Lord, and we all prayed to Him as well as we could to restore them to health. And He, seeing there was no other way of getting those people to help us so that we might be saved from our miserable existence, had mercy upon us, and in the morning all woke up well and hearty and went away in such good health as if they never had had any ailment whatever."

The news of miraculous cures spread fast. Each day more ailing Indians arrived, bringing gifts of venison, prickly pears, even deer hide, all certain that the Christions would cure them of their afflictions. And the miracles continued. Because of the great crowds of patients, the three worked hurriedly, and the gifts mounted in front of them. The cured natives celebrated their regained health with dances that often lasted through the night, and kept the exhausted Spaniards awake.

Winter was coming, and with it the end of the prickly pears and the beginning of the season of hunger. The Spaniards were advised not to leave the tribe. Going into an unknown, sparsely populated part of the country during general famine would be foolish. Sometimes, to the four who were eager to continue their journey, the advice sounded more like orders to stay. They felt themselves to be prisoners of their gracious hosts. Nevertheless, the respectful attitude of the Avavares continued; they were convinced by the continuous cures that the four were not merely medicine men but supernatural beings who had come to them in some mysterious way from the sky.

The four, together with the Avavares began to wander through the countryside in search of food. "All over the land are vast and handsome pastures, with good grass for cattle, and it strikes me the soil would be very fertile were the country inhabited and improved by reasonable people." Cabeza de Vaca was probably writing about the part of Texas that would, in two hundred years, become the great cattle producing country.

"We remained with the Avavares Indians for 8 months, according to our reckoning of the moons. During that time they came to us from many places and said that verily we were children of the sun." For these Indians, the sun was the giver of life, the everlasting mystery, the greatest power, their god. Nothing seemed to them more worthy of homage than this heavenly light; and no one more worthy of being connected with it than the four men.

Estebanico was the last to be enlisted in the actual performing of cures. ". . . but we found ourselves so pressed by the Indians coming from all sides that all of us had to become medicine men. I was the most daring and reckless of all in undertaking the cures. We never treated anyone that did not afterwards say he was well, and they had such confidence in our skill as to believe that none of them would die as long as we were among them."

When there were no sick to cure, the "sons of the sun" had to perform the same chores as the natives; and together with them, they suffered from exposure. "We went naked, and not being accustomed to it, like snakes we shed our skin twice a year. Exposure to the sun and air covered our chests and backs with big sores that made it very painful to carry the big and heavy loads, the ropes of which cut into the flesh of our arms."

One day, while they were out hunting for food along the Guadalupe River, Cabeza de Vaca wandered away from the others and was unable to find them again. The night was cruelly cold, and he was certain that he would not live to see the break of day. He was weak with hunger, naked, and shivering with cold, when suddenly he saw in front of him a burning tree. He spent the night beneath the warmth of the plant, and in the morning resumed the search for his companions, no longer in danger from cold because he carried with him a burning branch.

His search went on for four days and four nights. With him as he went, he carried a supply of dry branches, "ever with my fire and my load; for if the wood had failed me where none should be found, as many parts are without any, though I might have sought sticks elsewhere, there would have been no fire to kindle them. . . . All this while I tasted not a mouthful, nor did I find anything I could eat. My feet were bare and bled a good deal."

Finally, on the fifth day he found the Avavares' camp, where his companions had given him up for dead. Their rejoicing over his miraculous return was exceeded only by their awe at the even more miraculous tree of fire.

Unexplained and wondrous things kept happening, making all those who witnessed the events fearful of the unknown power inside the four men. One day a Susola Indian rushed into the Avavare camp, begging the Christians to come to the bedside of a dying man.

"I will not go," Castillo said. "It is one thing to cure the sick, but it is another to raise people from the dead."

"But we don't know if the man is dead." Dorantes said.

"He's dying; and before we can reach him, he will certainly be dead." Castillo's voice trembled, and he looked away from his friends. "One mistake, one disappointment, and they will have us killed as quickly as they accepted us."

"I'll go," Cabeza de Vaca said quietly.

"I'll go with you," Dorantes said.

"And I will, too," Estebanico added.

By the time the three reached the man's hut, they knew they had come too late. All of the dead man's possessions, and his house, had been set aflame, for such was the custom when death visited one of the tribe.

The body was outside, covered with a mat. Cabeza de Vaca knelt down and saw the man's "eyes rolled up, and the pulse gone, he having all the appearances of death, as they seemed to me and as Dorantes said."

But the Indians gathered over the corpse seemed to implore him silently to do something. They cried and

80

moaned as if their sorrow at the loss was unbearable. Cabeza de Vaca made the sign of the cross and began to pray passionately. Then, he began to administer mouth to mouth resuscitation, a remedy known to the Indians. His efforts seemed vain, but the Indians acknowledged his labor by presenting him with the bow that had belonged to the dead man and some prickly pears.

That same wintry night several Susolas woke the Spaniards with the happy report that the corpse had "got up whole and walked, had eaten and spoken. . . . This caused great wonder and fear, and throughout the land the people talked of nothing else. All to whom the fame of it reached, came to seek us that we should cure them and bless their children."

At the end of eight months, when the weather became warm, the four men again found themselves planning an escape. They knew that the Avavares would not let them go willingly; but they had to resume their journey. Too much time had already been wasted.

Cabeza de Vaca and Estebanico often stole out of the camp, exploring the land for miles around, charting their course. The first stop, they decided would be with the neighboring tribe, the Maliacones Indians. From there they would continue westward. Convinced now that God, for some purpose they could not fathom, wanted to preserve them from death and would continue to give them the ability to cure, they felt certain they would find welcome wherever they went. As children of the sun, their safety seemed assured.

In the middle of May, 1535, the four were ready to resume their journey.

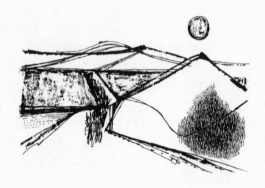

9

Slipping away from their hosts' camp during the night, the four men reached the tribe of Maliacones the next day. Their welcome was warm, though once again the friendliness of the people threatened to imprison them. The men hurried off, coming at last to a village inhabited by another tribe, the Arbadaos. Here they found starvation. The people were, "weak and lame and swollen so much as to cause us great astonishment." Their own hunger was acute, and they traded their cures for two small and bony dogs, which they cooked and ate.

Their course led north. They felt no fear as they crossed a land never before penetrated by a white man. All four, even Estebanico, believed deeply in God's special protection. In his mysterious way, he wanted them to survive, they felt sure. More than that, they thought that the price of their own survival was the use of the gift that had been granted to them, the ability to cure the sick and comfort the poor.

To substantiate their beliefs, their reception was invariably cordial. The natives, who knew little of kindness in their perpetual struggle to keep alive, always displayed great happiness at the sight of the four "children of the sun." When the time came for them to leave a village, the entire population would lament so loudly that the four men, too, felt great sorrow. During these days of travel among people so simple and yet so appreciative, a great love for the Indians took deep root in Cabeza de Vaca. It was to be a part of him for as long as he lived.

As they went from settlement to settlement, "the Indians brought us their sick, beseeching us that we would bless them. They gave us of what they had to eat . . . and were happy to be without anything to eat, that they might have food to give us. . . . We reached a hundred Indian huts, and as we approached, the people came out to receive us, shouting frightfully and slapping their thighs. They carried perforated gourds filled with pebbles, which are ceremonial objects of great importance. They only use them at dances, or as medicine, to cure, and nobody dares touch them but themselves."

The reputation of the four men grew until at last they were no longer traveling alone. They were followed by those who could not bear to be apart from them. The number of these followers—men, women, and children of different tribes—increased daily until it reached into the hundreds. All of these people had been born with an intense instinct for survival. And that instinct now turned them into crafty exploiters.

"While we were received very well everywhere, those who came with us would treat those who received us badly, taking away their belongings and plundering their homes, without leaving them anything. It grieved us very much to see how those who were so good to us were abused. Besides, we dreaded lest their behavior might cause trouble and strife. But as we could not venture to interfere or punish the transgressors, we had to wait until we might have more authority over them. Furthermore, the sufferers themselves, noticing how we felt, comforted us by saying we should not worry; that they were so happy at seeing us as to gladly lose their own considering it to be well employed and besides, that further on they would repay themselves from other Indians who were very rich. On that whole journey we were very worried by the number of people following us. We could not escape them, although we tried, because they were so anxious to touch us."

The word of the great crew of plunderers spread, but did not affect the love the Indians felt for the four men.

"As soon as we would arrive those that went with us would sack the houses of the others; but as these knew the custom before our coming, they hid some of their chattels and, after receiving us with much rejoicing, they took out the things which they had concealed and presented them to us. These were beads and ochre and several little bags of mica. We, following the custom, turned the gifts immediately over to the Indians who had come in our company."

84

With time, the procession became a riotous mob; its shouts and laughter, the women's chattering, the children's giggling, the men's arguments, and the screams of welcome all merged into an incessant noise that penetrated the forests, overflowed the valleys, and crossed the mountains, making this march not unlike a continuous, mad Mardi Gras. And, leading this mob that now numbered three to four thousand people, were four men whose prestige and power had grown until no one but they doubted that they were gods who were leading the Indians into a promised land of food and wealth.

"So great had become our authority that no one dared to drink without our permission. Indeed, whatever they either killed or found was put before us, without themselves daring to take anything until we had blessed it, though they should be expiring of hunger, they having so established the rule since marching with us."

Estebanico was the only one among the "children of the sun" who really enjoyed the maddening noise of the crowd, the robberies, the gossiping, the exaggerations. His love of the people who were with them was evident in his black eyes, which shone always and seemed to explode at the sight of a pretty Indian maiden.

Cabeza de Vaca, Dorantes, and Castillo were so revered by the Indians that they were approached only for cures. It was Estebanico who talked with the natives to find out the best trails and to gather information as to what lay ahead. Most of the time no one knew. To the west lay the setting sun; to the north lay dreaded hostile tribes. This was the end of their knowledge.

Gradually, however, inside the minds of the Spaniards new dreams of wealth were conceived and nourished by some of the stories that were told them and by some of the gifts they received. Dorantes was given a copper rattle that was said to have come from far away where mountains shone with gold and rivers ran with silver. They heard of the Seven Cities of Cíbola, cities that were filled with tall houses and thousands of people. But no one quite knew the way to them. And Cabeza de Vaca put less faith in the stories than either Castillo or Dorantes. He believed that they were going north to an unexplored sea and that riches would not be part of their discovery. He had seen too much bleak poverty about him to have illusions about great hidden wealth. He saw in the vast expanse of the land a future, but, it was a future that held primarily hard work and hardships, dangers and privations. He also foresaw difficulty in overcoming the Indians.

"Their eyesight, hearing, and senses in general are better, I believe, than those of any other men upon earth. They can stand, and have to stand, much hunger, thirst, and cold, being more accustomed and used to it than others. This I wish to state here, since, besides that all men are curious to know the habits and devices of others, such as might come in contact with these people should be informed of their customs and deeds, which will be of no small profit to them."

He was writing of the Comanches and the Apaches, two tribes that in 1535 were not the fierce warriors they would become later.

One night "we arrived at many houses seated on the banks of a beautiful river." They were on the shores of the Rio Grande River. Here they first came across the nourishing pine nuts, and here Cabeza de Vaca per-

86

formed his most amazing surgical feat. "Here they brought to me a man who, they told, a long time ago had been shot through the left side of the back with an arrow, the head of which struck close to his heart. He said it gave him much pain, and that on this account he was sick. I touched the region of the body and felt the arrowhead, and that it had pierced the cartilage. So, with a knife, I cut open the breast as far as the place. The arrow point had gotten athwart and was very difficult to remove. By cutting deeper and inserting the point of the knife with great difficulty, I got it out. It was very long. Then, with a deer bone, according to my knowledge of surgery, I made two stitches. After I had extracted the arrow they begged me for it, and I gave it to them. The whole village came back to look at it, and they sent it further inland that the people there might see it, too.

"On account of this cure, they made many dances and festivities, as is their custom. The next day I cut the stitches and the Indian was well. The cut I had made showed only a scar like a line in the palm of the hand, and he said that he felt not the least pain.

"Now this cure gave us such fame among them all over the country as they were capable of conceiving and respecting. . . . After leaving these people we traveled among so many different tribes and languages that nobody's memory can recall them all, and always they robbed each other; but those who lost and those who gained were equally content. . . . Often we had with us three to four thousand persons, and it was very tiresome to have to breathe on and make the sign of the cross over every morsel they ate or drank. For many other things which they wanted to do, they would come to ask our permission, so that it is easy to realize how greatly we were bothered."

Crossing the Rio Grande once more, not far from today's city of El Paso, Texas, the Indians grew fearful of hostile tribes. But even more than hostile tribes, they feared marching north. There, they said, there was nothing to eat, there were no people of any kind, and there could be no end to the journey but death. This unwillingness to go north angered Cabeza de Vaca so much that he left the camp in a huff to spend the night alone. "But directly they came to where I was and remained all night without sleep, talking to me in great fear, telling me how terrified they were, beseeching us to be no longer angry, and said that they would lead us in the direction it was our wish to go, though they knew they should die on the way."

The following morning "many fell sick and on the next day eight died. All over the country, when it was known, they became so afraid that it seemed as if the mere sight of us would kill them. . . . They believed we caused their death only by willing it, when in truth it gave us so much pain that it could not be greater; for, beyond their loss, we feared they might all die, or abandon us of fright, and that other people thenceforward would do the same, seeing what had come to these."

The four men were no less frightened by this mysterious illness than the natives. The prospect of being left completely alone, or attacked, or made slaves again, left them sleepless.

Those who were ill were cared for by their families

with great tenderness; but when any died, the relatives turned away from them. "Neither did they weep nor speak among themselves, make any signs, nor dare approach the bodies until we commanded these to be taken to burial."

For two days and two nights the Indians and the Christians lived lives of terror. "We prayed to God, Our Lord, to relieve them; and from that time the sick began to get better." As suddenly as it had come, the illness disappeared; and once again plans were made to go northward. Those still convalescing were ordered to remain behind until they were well enough to travel. The others set off, a solemn, silent people, ignorant of what lay ahead, fearful of enemies and of the unknown in a world suddenly grown evil.

They traveled for fifteen days. The silence hovered over them. "One child, who had begun to cry, was carried off some distance and with some very sharp mice-teeth they scratched it from shoulders down to nearly the legs." Angered by this act of cruelty, Cabeza de Vaca demanded an explanation. ". . . they said it was done to punish the child for having wept in my presence." But it was fear of the Jumanos, in whose territory the wanderers were, that made the Indians jumpy. For years those who traveled with the Spanish had fought the Jumanos, and now they were walking straight into their country, without weapons. Nevertheless, the Indians had no intention of doing anything but following the four men until ordered to turn back or to die in their defense.

Castillo and Estebanico were sent ahead to scout the hostile land. When they rejoined the others, Castillo "told how he had found permanent houses inhabited, and the people of which ate beans and squashes and that he had also seen maize. Of all the things upon earth, this caused us the greatest pleasure." Their joy at finding permanent structures in a land of nomadic tribes was a joy born of the fact that now they knew the land could be used. Adobe houses and cultivation of vegetables meant stability. This, then, could be a land that Spain could colonize.

The people who had followed the Christians so long were now persuaded by Cabeza de Vaca to turn back. He feared that an encounter with the Jumanos might result in open warfare. And this, above all things, he did not want. He could not bear to think either of his Indians being hurt, or of his chances of coming to know the pueblo dwellers being destroyed. He felt he must approach these new people in friendship, for he recognized that they could comprehend much more than any Indians he had met and be prepared for the coming of Spanish colonists.

The good-bys were tearful. Every man, woman, and child who was leaving the company of the Spaniards had to be blessed and a cross made over him. The four men gave away every last shred of personal belongings to the Indians, who wanted some part of the men to remain with them forever. As the four watched their friends go back to a life in which all time and effort was needed to stay barely alive, they felt that indeed these people were taking with them a part of each. And for the four, there were memories, too, that would not die, years that were incredible in both their horror and their beauty. Tears streamed down their sunburned faces.

10

The Jumanos received the four men with great ceremony and gave them "beans and many squashes to eat, gourds to carry water in, robes of cowhide, and other things." They stayed in the pueblo for several days. Here, for the first time in all their travels, they were with a people whose culture was advanced enough that they could appreciate words as well as deeds.

"We told them, by signs which they understood, that in Heaven there was a . . . God . . . who had created Heaven and earth, and whom we worshipped as Our Lord; that we did as He ordered us to do, all good things coming from His hand, and that if they were to do the same they would become very happy; and so well were they inclined that, had there been a language in which we could have made ourselves perfectly understood, we would have left them all Christians."

Forty-seven years later, in 1582, Antonio de Espejo wrote a description of these same people and the impact the visit of Cabeza de Vaca and the others had had on them:

"These people are all clothed and seemed to have some light of our holy faith; for they made signs of God, looking up towards Heaven, and call him in their language *Apalito*, and acknowledge him for their Lord, from whose bountiful land and mercy they confess that they have received their life and being, and these worldly goods. Many of them with their wives and children came unto the friar that he might cross and bless them. When demanding of them, from whom they had received that knowledge of God, they answered, from three Christions and one Negro which passed that way, and remained certain days among them, who by the signs which they made, were Alvar Núñez Cabeza de Vaca, and Dorantes, and Castillo Maldoñado, and a Negro; all of which escaped of the company which Pánfilo de Nárvaez landed in Florida; who, after they had been many days captives and slaves, escaped and came to these towns, by whom God showed many miracles, and healed only by the touching of their hands many sick persons, by reason thereof they became very famous in all that country."

After the visit at the first Pueblo, the Spaniards and the Moor were surrounded by a new people, with whom they went to "other settlements. And thence on we found a new custom. The people who heard of our approach did not, as before, come out to meet us on the way, but we found them at their homes, and they had other houses ready for us. They were all seated with their faces turned to the wall, their heads bowed and the hair pulled over the eyes. Their belongings had been gathered in a heap in the middle of the floor and thence on they began to give us many robes of skins. There was nothing they would not give us. They are the best formed people, liveliest and most capable, who best understood us and answered our questions. . . . Among those people we found the women better treated than in any other part of the Indies as far as we have seen. They wear skirts of cotton that reach as far as the knee, and over them half-sleeves of scraped deerskin with strips that hang down to the ground and which they clean with a certain root, that cleans very well and this keeps them tidy."

Lack of rain was the curse of these people. "They begged us to ask Heaven" for it. As the men traveled on, they suffered great hunger, and they came upon a "people who, for one third of the year, eat but powdered straw."

In the desert through which they moved there was but one trail to follow; it led from one water hole to the next. "While traveling, we went without food all day until night, and we ate so little as to astonish them. We never felt exhaustion, neither were we in fact at all weary, so inured were we to hardship. We possessed great influence and authority; to preserve both we seldom talked with them. The Negro was in constant conversation; he informed himself about the ways we wished to take, of the towns there were, and the matter we desired to know."

Once again, the four, bearded men, esteemed as prophets from a mysterious country, were followed by

93

a crowd that often numbered three thousand, including many who were very old and sick. "Women in labor would fall out of the procession, and would appear an hour later with a new human being to be blessed. Mothers would bring tiny babies, taught to hold three kernels in their fists; for they believed that if the white men would accept this gift of corn, the baby making the present would never be sick." [1]

The Jumanos led the explorers to a country inhabited by many different tribes. These lands lay somewhat to the southwest. "In that part of the country those who were at war would at once make peace and become friendly to each other, in order to meet us and bring us all they possessed; and thus we left the whole country at peace."

There have been few conquests more peaceable than that of the "children of the sun." Wanting nothing, they were given everything. Carrying no weapons, they were true peacemakers. Giving freely of their faith and their goodness, they planted in those they met a belief in the Supreme Being who was good as well as powerful, and a love of other men. Those who came near them were convinced that all four were beings of utmost kindness and need never be feared.

Moving south, they came into the irrigated Sonora Valley, to the present site of the town of Ures. The inhabitants of the village there offered them six hundred hearts of deer and other gifts, including five emeralds that had been made into arrowheads. "I asked where they got these; and they said the stones were brought from

[1] Morris Bishop, *Odyssey of Cabeza de Vaca*

some lofty mountains that stand toward the north, where were populous towns and very large houses, and they were purchased with plumes and the feathers of parrots." They were probably referring to the Arizona and New Mexico pueblos, but later other Spaniards who invented dreams of riches and pursued them as if they were reality, thought of them as the Seven Cities of Cibola and searched for them in vain throughout the western part of what is now the United States.

The four men were now but a few miles from the Gulf of California. The Indians told them of the sea and its desolate coastline where nothing grew and where the people were "very shy and sourly." The men, who thought they had come to the South Sea, decided against following the coast, and walked directly south after leaving the "Village of the Hearts."

Their route led across the Yaqui River, which was in flood; so their journey was delayed for two weeks on its banks. During that time, hundreds of natives visited their camp. On one, Castillo noticed a sword buckle, and, sewn to it, a horseshoe nail. Castillo at once went to his friends with his discovery. They dared not show their great excitement for the Indians believed them to be gods and therefore to have no connection with other white men. But quietly, without raising the suspicions of the Indians, the three Spaniards inquired about the origin of the buckle. They were told that its previous owner rode an enormous dragon; that he was bearded and wore shiny clothes; and that he came with other white men, killed two Indians, and went away. The Indians explained further that the white men "had gone to sea, putting their lances beneath the water, and going themselves under water; afterwards they were seen on the surface going towards the sunset." The explanation eliminated the probability of a nearby Spanish settlement. It was obvious that the visitors had come by ship and had sailed away. It pained Cabeza de Vaca to think that they found it necessary to take two lives.

Shortly thereafter the flood subsided and their journey began again. Further south the joyful anticipation Cabeza de Vaca had felt at the prospect of seeing his countrymen changed to sadness and anger. Tales of burned villages, men hung from trees, buzzards feasting on them, and of panic stricken Indians reached the marchers. It was clear that slave-raiding parties were ahead. Overnight, those who were traveling with the four, became fearful for their safety.

Each day news of new terror came to them. Pained and disheartened, Cabeza de Vaca tried to talk the Indians with him into turning back. He did not succeed. "At that time we had Indians with us belonging a hundred leagues behind, and we could not persuade them to return to their homes." The uneasiness of the Indians instead changed to a fear of leaving him. They were all certain that as long as they remained with their four leaders nothing could harm them. Cabeza de Vaca's arguments that they might well be taken as slaves, did not shake their faith.

"We traveled over a great part of the country and found it all deserted, as the people had fled to the mountains, leaving houses and fields out of fear of the Christians. This filled our hearts with sorrow, seeing the land so fertile and beautiful, so full of water and streams, but abandoned, the places burned down, and the people so

96

thin and wan, fleeing and hiding; and as they did not raise any crops, the destitution had become so great that they ate tree-barks and roots. . . . They brought us blankets which they had been concealing from the Christians and gave them to us, and told us how the Christians had penetrated into the country before, and had destroyed and burned the villages, taking with them half of the men and all the women and children and how those who could, escaped by flight. . . . They took us to a village on a crest of a mountain, which can be reached only by a very steep trail, where we found a great many people who had gathered there out of dread of the Christians."

That night, on the top of the mountain, Cabeza de Vaca swore that he would spend the rest of his life fighting those who made slaves of the Indians. He felt that he had been miraculously preserved from death, and the reason for this was now obvious to him. The closer he came to his countrymen, the clearer it became that he had to stand against them, against their injustice, against the destruction they brought with them. He would be the spokesman, the champion of the wronged Indians. That night he promised God and himself that he would never rest until the fight was won, until kindness replaced greed and love conquered hatred.

The next morning, taking eleven Indians and Estebanico, he set off in pursuit of the slave hunters. The very next day, a day in early March of 1536, near the Sinaloa River, he met the first Spaniards, "four Christians on horseback, who, seeing me in such a strange attire and in company with Indians were greatly startled. They stared at me for quite a while, speechless." When he spoke to the soldiers in Spanish, they jumped from their horses and, to the great astonishment of the Indians present, embraced him; he in turn cried and clung to them. They were the first Spaniards, aside from his two companions and Oviedo, that he had seen in eight years.

The four soldiers guided Cabeza de Vaca and his men along the banks of the river to their camp and their commanding officer, Captain Diego de Alcaraz.

Captain Alcaraz was described by a contemporary as "a man unfitted to have people under his command." He was shrewd, but not intelligent; he was cruel and greedy; he had little feeling for anyone or anything but the profit that would be his from successful raids on the Indians. Those he captured were sent to the Governor of the province of Pánuco, Nuño Beltran de Guzmán, who in turn sold them to mine operators and landholders throughout the West Indies. Guzmán had a reputation for dishonesty, arrogance, cruelty, and flagrant violations of the law that forbade the practice of slavery.

When Captain Alcaraz first saw Cabeza de Vaca, he thought him a madman, a deserter who had gotten lost in the wilds of the Indian country. He listened to his story, but having never heard of Nárvaez expedition to Florida, gave it little credence. What did impress him was the fact that the madman was traveling with a handful of Indians and that he had apparently spent enough time among the natives to gain their confidence. He could use him, he decided, as a decoy for hunting slaves. When Cabeza de Vaca told him that two of his companions were waiting several miles away with a crowd of six hundred Indians, the captain's eyes brightened with greed. Here was a haul that would certainly rate him a promotion. He offered to send a detachment of soldiers and several natives to bring Dorantes, Castillo and the multitude to the camp. Cabeza de Vaca dispatched Estebanico to act as a guide.

During the five days that followed Cabeza de Vaca had "many and bitter quarrels" with Captain Alcaraz. When the great crowd came, Cabeza de Vaca still feared greatly for the safety of the Indians, and begged them to return to their homes. The Indians flatly refused to do so, wishing to conduct the four men safely to the next tribe, as had been the custom. Alcaraz grew furious over Cabeza de Vaca's promises that no harm would come to the Indians and was even more furious at his power over them. Alcaraz had believed that it would be an easy matter to enslave the six hundred natives; instead he was faced with people who were willing to serve a madman and his three companions, but completely unwilling to even recognize his official presence and authority.

"At all this the Christians were greatly vexed and told their own interpreter to say to the Indians how we were of their own race, but had gone astray for a long while, and were people of no luck and little heart, whereas they were the lords of the land, whom they should obey and serve. The Indians gave all that talk of theirs little attention. They parlayed among themselves, saying that the Christians lied, for we had come from sunrise, while the others came from where the sun sets; that we cured the sick, while the others killed those who were healthy; that we went naked and shoeless, whereas the others wore clothes and went on horseback with lances. Also, that we asked for nothing, but gave away all we were presented with; meanwhile the others seemed to have no other aim than to steal what they could, and never gave anything to anybody. In short, they recalled all our deeds and praised them highly, contrasting them with the conduct of the others. This they told the interpreter of the Christians (in language Primahaity, which they spoke for 400 leagues). Finally, we never could convince the Indians that we belonged to the other Christians, and only with much trouble and insistence could we prevail upon them to go home." They "told us they would do what we commanded, and would build their towns, if the Christians would suffer them."

The Indians lined up sadly so that the three Spaniards might make over them the sign of the cross. Cabeza de Vaca knew the Indians had faith in his ability to keep them safe as they journeyed home. Their eyes shone with trust, and he felt that he would gladly put up his own life in defence of theirs. As he watched them slowly walk away he was seized with an almost intolerable love for them. And he recognized, too, that it was very likely that the men under Captain Alcaraz would "fall upon the Indians we had sent back in fancied security and in peace."

This, of course, was exactly what Alcaraz planned to do. But he wanted Cabeza de Vaca and his companions out of his way before he attempted the wholesale enslavement. He took into his confidence, a Lieutenant Cabreros and ordered him to guide the four men, on the pretext of taking them to the governor, away from any Indian settlements and finally to lose them in the desert. Cabreros not only lost the four men, but himself and his soldiers as well. The march covered seventy-five miles, and seven men perished of thirst.

At last Cabeza de Vaca learned of the treachery of Alcaraz and would have vented his fury on Cabreros had not the lieutenant already abandoned them. Unable to continue the deception, he had fled to Culiacán, and there he confessed everything to Vice-Governor Mechior Díaz. Díaz saddled his horse immediately and rode out to meet the four survivors of the Nárvaez expedition. The meeting between them was highly emotional. Díaz, a gentle, honorable man "wept with us, giving praises to God our Lord for having extended over us so great care. He comforted and entertained us hospitably. In behalf of the governor, Nuño de Guzmán, and himself, he tendered all that he had and all the service in his power. He showed much regret for the seizure and the injustice we had received from Alcaraz and others."

For the first time in eight years the four men were to spend the night in beds, between sheets. If they had had a dream of doing so during their long years of privation, they were disappointed by its fulfillment. Not one of them could sleep in a bed; not one could stand the touch of a sheet on his rough body. All four spent that first night, and the nights that followed, sleeping on the bare floor under deerskins. Civilization held other disappointments for them. Their calloused feet could not take the feel of shoes; their skins burned by the wind and the sun, the cold and the heat, could not get used to the touch of linen. The collar of a shirt felt as terrible as once the bites of insects had felt. It was several weeks before the four finally adjusted themselves to a way of life that had once been the only way they knew. And during those weeks they each came to realize the meaninglessness of many things they had thought important, and the importance of many things they had considered meaningless.

In Díaz, Cabeza de Vaca found an ally in his fight against slavery. The two decided to put an end to the shameful exploitation of the natives sanctioned by Governor Guzmán. It was their object to see to it that the natives were not molested by such men as Alcaraz. They decided to hold a great council of the Indians at which they would be promised protection from slave raiders if they would return to their villages. Two messengers who knew "the great authority and command we carried and exercised . . . the wonders we had worked, the sick we had cured, and the many things besides we had done," were dispatched, together with one of the sacred gourds given to the "children of the sun."

The Indians, although distrustful of the message, thinking that Cabeza de Vaca had been forced to trap them into the meeting, did send three chieftains. To them Cabeza de Vaca gave his word that slavery was unlawful and that it would no longer be tolerated. He begged them to spread the word among the Indians that their safety was now assured; and Díaz swore in front of them to uphold what Cabeza de Vaca had promised.

Soon the entire area around the place where the vice-governor lived and had met with the chieftains was filled with Indians. Dancing and celebration continued far into the nights, and gifts and food were exchanged by both sides as tokens of good will. The Indians promised to return to their native villages and there began building churches and cultivating the land.

Soon after Alcaraz himself came to the vice-governor to bring the news that peace seemed to have descended throughout the country. The six hundred Indians he had captured had been set free. They had settled on Rio Fuerte. Others had begun to plant crops and build churches. No man but Cabeza de Vaca could have achieved this transformation. Now, his conscience clear, his heart light, he could set off toward Mexico City and then Spain.

He had an aim now: to return to his native land and beg the King for an appointment to the Indies. He wanted to return in a position that would let him keep watch over the welfare of those who had come to trust him. He wanted to spend the rest of his life among the Indians, protecting them, living with them, teaching them.

On his way to Mexico City he stopped to face governor Guzmán, confronting him with a copy of his directive allowing the capture of Indians as slaves. Cabeza de Vaca vowed to make the document known to the proper authorities in Spain and threatened immediate discipline from Mexico City, should Guzmán fail to stop the raiding of Indian villages. The visit had the desired effect; Guzmán's profitable side-line as a slave trader came to an end.

As the four men moved closer to Mexico City, they were again followed by thousands of worshipping Indians. The fame of the men had proceeded them. As they entered Mexico City on July 24, some eight years and three months after landing on the coast of Florida, they gave "thanks to God for having saved us from so many calamities."

11

When he returned to Spain, in August, 1536, Cabeza de Vaca felt like a stranger in a foreign land. Jerez seemed like a grey prison of stones. The people, the noises, the houses, the very food he ate, got on his nerves. He wanted peace in which he could work on his *Relatión*; but there was no peace, only continual interruptions.

Men came night and day, seekers of information, men who wanted advice on how they could get rich. Telling them that he had come back with nothing was of no use. All believed a widespread fabricated tale of a hidden treasure he was keeping in Seville, though they discreetly avoided the subject in front of him. They wanted him to confirm stories they had heard of riches to be found north of Mexico. They would not believe that there were no riches. They had already heard tales of the Seven Cities of Cibola.

He who had come to love the continuous presence of thousands of Indians grew impatient at the sight of old friends. Human frailties, gossiping, false hopes, greed, and jealousy filled him with anger. The complicated warfare waged by Spain against Rome, France, Germany, Turkey, and Tunis bored him. He wanted only to finish his book, for it was the one thing he could give Charles V as a token of the trip, and the one way he could put forth his doctrine of peaceful conquest. On the book rested not only his future but also the future of all the Indians north of Mexico. Once finished, the book would go to the King; then, perhaps, he would receive an audience and could ask permission to go back as a protector of the natives. This was the one thing he wanted.

Few monarchs have had a more complex reign than Spain's Charles V. Crowned King and Emperor in October, 1520, he had to cope with eight independent parliaments, wars with several countries, the Reformation and numerous religious schisms, rebellions in conquered provinces, and the rapidly expanding colonies on the other side of the Atlantic.

By nature a conservative, he was considered weak by many, colorless and dictatorial by others. His European affairs took most of his attention and time, but his interests were really with the new lands, and his faith in the future of those lands was boundless. Because of that faith, his concern for the native population was considerable. He was totally opposed to slavery but realized his power to prevent it was weakened by the great distance between him and the colonists. He feared the men of the colonies with their newly acquired riches, for he knew that power and wealth can destroy loyalty and warp the mind. He disapproved of much his colonists were doing, yet he could not entirely oppose them for it was they who made Spain's expansion possible, and it was this expansion and the wealth it brought that paid for Spain's European wars.

Charles V read with great interest Cabeza de Vaca's account of his eight years in North America. He waited impatiently for a reunion with this unusual man. The audience lasted a long time. The King asked detailed questions about the Nárvaez expedition and listened to Cabeza de Vaca's plans for peaceful colonization. At the end of the long interview, the King assured Cabeza de Vaca that a high position of trust would soon be found for him in the Indies.

With such assurances, each day Cabeza de Vaca looked for the King's messenger. But days stretched into weeks, weeks into months, and months into years.

From the New World great news came of Pizzaro's conquest of Peru. The ex-swineherd from the province of Extremadura, had conquered with a mere handful of men, a golden kingdom. His accomplishment overshadowed Cortés's conquest of Mexico. Balboa had discovered the Pacific Ocean, and Hernando de Soto was given title to all the lands known as Florida and many islands in the Caribbean. With each new triumph, each new discovery, Cabeza de Vaca became more painfully aware of how far he was from accomplishing his one vowed goal.

News came from Mexico about his three companions: Dorantes had married a wealthy widow and had been given sizeable property in Mexico. Castillo had also married a wealthy woman and was living a peaceful life in Mexico City. Estebanico had been sent in search of the Seven Cities of Cibola. With two greyhounds and a great crowd of Indians, he had set out, basing his operation on Cabeza de Vaca's fame as a healer. But the trail had led nowhere, and its end was a Zuñi arrow.

Meanwhile, life for Cabeza de Vaca had come to a complete standstill. As he walked the cobblestone streets of Jerez and Seville, he longed for the deserts and mountains and rivers that he had once crossed. The food he ate, the soft bed he slept in, the clothes he wore, all exasperated him.

In 1537, Pope Paul III declared the Indians to be human beings and their enslavement to be punishable by excommunication. When Cabeza de Vaca heard this, he rejoiced, but he also despaired. It seemed that now he would not be needed by the Indians; and to help them was the one thing he wanted to do. But two years later Bartolomé de Las Casas came to Spain from the New World, and from him Cabeza de Vaca learned that laws, though made, are not always kept. Las Casas, the priest who had helped Cabeza de Vaca secure his appointment with Nárvaez, had fought almost alone for the rights of the Indians for years, and the Papal decree had not really helped him.

The two men, Las Casas and Cabeza de Vaca, spent hours together, talking and planning. They discussed their earlier meeting, and Cabeza de Vaca confessed what a great influence it had had on his future actions. They pondered over the problem of the Indians.

"I can't do anything for the natives just sitting here in Spain," Cabeza de Vaca exploded angrily one day.

"You'll go back soon," the priest said quietly. "But even if you never do go back," he added, "you have already done more than any other man for our common cause. Your book is being read and talked about, and all those who read it must realize that the natives you came in contact with are like children, children that need our protection and love."

Las Casas's words proved true. The scene for the return was set one September day in 1539. A badly battered Spanish galleon arrived from the region along the Rio de la Plata, an area in what is now part of Argentina and Paraguay. Felipe de Cáceres had come to ask for royal help for the settlers of Asunción, the only Spanish settlement south of the equator.

Charles V finally saw an opportunity to use Cabeza de Vaca. He appointed him Governor of Paraguay.

Cabeza de Vaca had heard of Cáceres, a vicious and cowardly man who, even now, in the King's court, bragged about the colonists' use of the natives. Such talk filled Cabeza de Vaca with anger and pain. But he felt only joy when he thought of going to a land where he would be able to punish men such as Cáceres and start a new era.

For three years he had felt like a warrior in a time of peace, but now his inactivity was coming to an end. Now at last he could care for and protect the misused people of a land where cruelty and greed alone seemed to motivate men's actions. Into that land he meant to bring tolerance and charity.

PART II

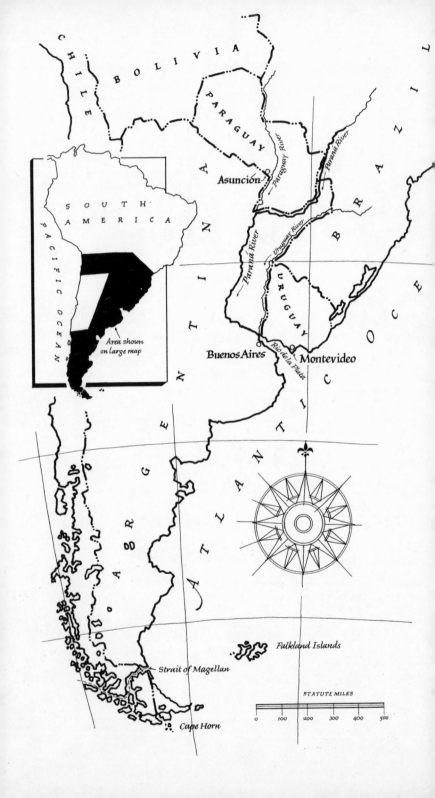

12

Throughout history, pioneers have felt a special kind of possessiveness for what they have gained by the agony and toil that the subduing of wilderness land requires. And few people have ever been more proud of their accomplishments and more possessive of their lands than the colonists in Paraguay's Asunción. At the time Cabeza de Vaca was sent there, it was the only Spanish foothold in South America below the equator. No land the Spanish had acquired had cost more in human suffering and human lives than this land, which stretched from the gigantic estuary of the second largest river system in South America, the Rio de la Plata, over the endless plains to the Andes, the tallest mountain range in the New World.

When the Spanish came, the region was sparsely populated by the Guaraní Indians, nomadic tribes of hunters and fishermen. They were Indians with an amazing weapon, the *boleador*. This sling-like device, whirled over the head to project a stone, was as accurate a weapon as a rifle. With it, the Guaranís could bring down a deer in full flight. The *boleador* and the land, itself, savage and beautiful, treacherous and fertile, prevented for a number of years the conquest of that part of South America. But all who took part in the attempt, including those who perished, were people determined as few invaders have ever been to defeat defeat itself.

The first discovery of the land came in 1516. In October of 1515, Juan de Solís, the Spanish Crown's chief pilot-explorer, set sail from Spain with three small ships and sixty men. His orders were to follow a southward course along the Atlantic coast of South America.

Five months later, in February, at the height of summer, since they were below the equator, de Solís's expedition entered what seemed to be an undiscovered sea. In reality this was the wide mouth of the Rio de la Plata. Because of its fresh water, de Solís named this body of water *El Mar Dulce* (The Sweet Sea).

The three ships sailed along the northern shore, along what is today Uruguay. Among the tall grass that stretched like another even more gigantic sea, de Solís and his men often saw savage-looking hunters. But as time went on, the savagery in the faces they saw seemed to diminish. So the first time the natives made friendly signs, de Solís and several of his men rowed a boat to land. Their feet touched the shore, and the Indians were upon them. Aboard ship, those left behind watched in wide-eyed horror as the Indians beat the Spaniards to death and began to devour their bodies. Many men wept, others were silent, as the ships turned back towards Spain.

Ten years went by before another explorer was courageous enough to wander into the green prairie of death.

Then Sebastian Cabot succeeded de Solís as the Crown's pilot, and it became his duty to take up the exploration of South America where de Solís had left it.

Cabot's ships were well equipped with both men and provisions when they sailed out of Spain in 1526. Cabot, whose temper was as short as his compassion, marooned four of his officers on an island off the coast of Brazil. But the expedition went on. Convinced that the Rio de la Plata was flowing from a silver source, Cabot spent three years navigating it, and its tributaries, finding nothing. He founded one settlement, Santi Espiritú, but it was abandoned by the time he, having lost half of his men, turned back to Spain. He was gone less than four years. His only return cargo was a report of lands where precious metals and jewels tumbled down from the mountains with greater force and abundance than flowed the streams that fed the Silver River.

Although many listened to these colored tales, it took money, and, it seemed, men willing to die, to launch an expedition to investigate. The man who volunteered to go finally, and at his own expense, was Don Pedro de Mendoza. The expedition that he took to the New World, which set sail on August 24, 1535, was extraordinary. It consisted of 14 vessels and 1500 men, among them many representatives of the finest of Spain's nobility. It was the first time that noblemen had been attracted to the newly discovered lands. Until then, only adventurers seeking quick fortunes, the poorer aristocracy, or those chased into adventure by actual hunger, had sailed into the unknown. But the noblemen who joined de Mendoza's expedition were so sure that they were going to live in a safe and beautiful land that many brought along their wives and children, their pets and their favorite mounts.

But once again a curse seemed to hang over anyone who wanted to tame the wilderness of the Rio de la Plata. The first hint of tragedy came when some of the men deserted in the Canaries; but it was not until the expedition touched the coast of Brazil and two ships turned and fled back to Spain, that the feeling of coming disaster intensified.

Don Pedro de Mendoza through the voyage had found the popularity of his second in command, Don Juan Osorio, increasingly hard to accept, especially since he, Mendoza, did not share that popularity. In his jealousy, he now blamed Osorio for the desertion of the two ships. Mendoza's favorite officer, Juan de Ayolas, flamed Mendoza into a rage.

"It is Osorio," Ayolas insisted. "It is he who undermines everyone's faith in you. He is responsible."

"I know," Mendoza shouted, "but I don't know what I can do about it."

"Why don't you leave it to me?" Ayolas was an ambitious man. And although his personal dream of riches and glory did not include de Mendoza, he was willing to take advantage of any situation to further his own ends.

The beach at what is now Rio de Janeiro stretched white in the moonlight that night. The ships were anchored; and most of the men, women, and children had gladly come to land after the long voyage. Their fires, for warmth and cooking, added a friendly glow to the moonlight. But Ayolas and a friend, Juan de Salazar de Espinosa, walked silently away from the fires. They both knew that Osorio had to be eliminated. But how? Leaving him behind was out of the question.

"It must be something more final than that," Ayolas said under his breath.

The cry of a wild bird broke the silence of the night, and each man, automatically, reached for his dagger. The feel of the cold metal under his hand sent a shudder through Ayolas. At the same moment a cloud passed over the moon, and from the darkness the voice of Osorio, who was standing watch, was heard:

"Who goes?"

Their hands still on their daggers, both men turned. Osorio's last cry died in his throat as the steel of two blades entered his heart. Three times Ayolas stabbed the body of the already dead man.

The deed could not be hidden. Don Pedro de Mendoza was pleased, no one could protest, and the expedition went on without Osorio.

It was December, four months after the expedition had started from Spain, when the Rio de la Plata was sighted. A strong breeze came from the endless plains, carrying with it the smell of earth to those sick of the sea. The ships sailed up the broad waterway and stopped finally on the south shore, not too far from the juncture of the Paraná and the Uruguay Rivers, which together form the Rio de la Plata.

"We shall build a city here," Mendoza decided, "and call it Santa María de Buenos Aires."

The city was built: a city of mud huts with roofs thatched with reeds, surrounded by a mud wall, for the plain yielded neither timber nor stones. The nobles discarded their fine clothes, and for the first time in their lives dirtied their hands with work. Even the women and the children helped to erect this crude outpost on the edge of the grassland, facing toward the sea from which they had come.

At first the natives stared from the safety of distance; they watched the building of something they had never felt the need of, permanent homes. Then came a day when an offering of fish and game was made. The Spaniards accepted these happily, and in exchange offered the Indians trinkets, beads, mirrors, and colorful bits of cloth. But as weeks went by, the supplies the Spaniards had brought with them dwindled, and the food the Indians brought was not sufficient to feed everyone. The Spaniards asked for more offerings, although they no longer had anything to give the Indians in exchange, for all the trinkets had been distributed. The natives instead came more rarely; the strangers no longer fascinated them. In desperation, Mendoza had the local chieftain brought in by force and demanded that the Indians continue to provide fish and meat. The chieftain refused.

"There is no other way," Ayolas said to Mendoza. "We must make the Indians our slaves. As slaves they will have to do as they are told."

Don Pedro wanted to delay any outright battle with the natives. He hoped that they would come back with provisions, that there would be no need for war or slavery. But by Corpus Christi Day, 1536, when the Spaniards had been at Buenos Aires for six months, everyone knew that something had to be done. Famine was setting in.

"I have decided," Pedro de Mendoza told his gathered officers, "to chastise the natives. We are no longer in a position to bargain with them. Empty threats will not do. I propose to teach them a lesson. We'll frighten them by attacking them at their own camp. We have plenty of firearms, swords, and horses. With these weapons, we will subdue them into servitude."

He appointed his brother Diego to head an expedition of 330 men, 80 of them on horseback. The Spanish counted on terrorizing the Indians with the horses; but the natives were used to the animals, having seen them around Buenos Aires. What the Spanish did not count on was the swamp that separated them from the Indian camp.

The swamp held the Spanish prisoner while the Indians picked them off, one by one, like targets, with *boleadors*. The Spaniards who managed to get out of the swamp attacked the Indians with swords and killed a few, but the battle did not last through the day. At evening eighty-five survivors staggered back to Buenos Aires. Diego de Mendoza was among the great majority of those who had set out, the ones who never returned.

Not one horse came back. In the swamp, struggling for footing, many of them shed their masters for the tall grass of the prairies. They pushed through the wounded and the fallen, across the swamp, away from the Indian camp, toward freedom. From the four or five dozen that reached the prairie before they were killed, sprang the hordes that later made Argentina famous. They were the very first horses in South America, and they multiplied and lived off the wilderness until, centuries later, the *gauchos* herded them together to serve man once again.

The Indians were not satisfied with victory in one battle. Led by the fierce Guaranís, several tribes attacked the city of Buenos Aires. After setting fire to the thatched roofs, they also set aflame four of the ships. But they did not enter the mud-walled fort and kill off the Spaniards, who waited there in terror. Had the Indians done so, the Spanish would have been saved from the horrors of sickness and starvation that followed.

The winter that settled in soon after was a long nightmare of pestilence and hunger. Desperate for food, two soldiers killed a horse, one of the few not sent to the ill-fated battle, for meat and were promptly hung. That night the men's bodies were cut off and devoured. Those families who had brought with them pets, dogs and cats, had to guard them day and night. But neither the dogs nor the cats escaped; even rats were hunted and eaten. The prairie around Buenos Aires offered nothing, and to venture far into it meant certain death from the *boleador*. Only fish, caught by those still strong to wade into the waters, provided some sustenance.

With the coming of Spring, only five hundred and sixty people were alive. Mendoza decided to ascend the Rio de la Plata and then the Paraná. With four hundred people he reached the site of Cabot's settlement, Santi

Espiritú, now overgrown with jungle. The Spaniards, sick in both body and spirit, were afraid to venture further inland. As it was fifty more had died since they set out. Once back in Buenos Aires, Don Pedro was ready to sail back to Spain.

"I'll beg the King for help," he promised Ayolas, who had volunteered to stay. "In the meantime, I appoint you governor of these lands."

When Mendoza set sail late in 1536, accompanied by women, children, and a handful of the sick and desperately discouraged, he was already deathly sick with fever. During the voyage he prayed that he would live long enough to demand help from the King for those he had left behind. But he died before reaching Spain and was buried at sea. Those who survived the voyage presented themselves before the Council of the Indies and begged in his place for the help that Ayolas so greatly needed. The plea was heeded, and three vessels under the command of Alonso Cabrera were dispatched. They carried, among other things, a general pardon for the colonists who had eaten of human flesh.

Meanwhile, Ayolas did not wait for help, but with a small contingent of men sailed immediately up the Paraná River, into the country of the Guaranís. Sailing beyond Santi Espritú, the Spaniards were amazed at the abundance of game, fish, and even cultivated vegetables. At first they did not risk encounter with the Guaranís, but kept to their vessels. As the ship sailed on into the lush tropics, however, the Spanish became more trusting of the Guaranís.

On February 2, 1537, Candlemas Day, Ayolas established a settlement and called it Candelaría. This was not to be the end of the journey, however. He was determined to sail on as long as necessary to find the land of silver and gold, but he was mindful of the royal orders to establish settlements whenever possible. It was through settlements that Spain hoped to hold onto the lands its citizens were discovering.

Ayolas was sure that it was he who would discover the fabulous *El Dorado*, land of untold wealth, that previous explorers had heard whispers of; but not one of the Indians who voluntarily came to the settlement wished to talk about it. One day, when he had almost given up hope of ever having a guide to show him the way, an Indian with a smattering of Spanish arrived at his quarters.

"Where did you learn our language?" Ayolas inquired.

"From Señor García," the Indian replied.

"There are many Garcías among us, what is his full name and where did you meet him? Were you his slave?

"I was no slave to him," the Indian replied with dignity. "I guide him. And his name was Alejo García."

"Alejo García!" Ayolas exclaimed. Alejo García had been with de Solís. There had been reports that five of de Solís's men had escaped massacre and found a land of fabulous wealth. This was part of the tale of *El Dorado;* and here was proof of its truth.

"*Si, señor,* I was with him in *El Dorado* and until his death."

Ayolas' hand trembled. This man, probably this man alone among all men, could lead him to the land of silver and gold he sought, the land of unbelievable riches.

An expedition would leave at once. He would take most of his best men, the strongest soldiers; but he would leave Domingo Martínez de Irala in charge of the settlement and the boats. The Indians would not attack him on the journey, he was sure, for they would know that there were other white men awaiting his return, men in Candelaría, men in Buenos Aires, and more men coming from across the sea.

Before he set off with the Indian guide, in one vessel with 130 men, Ayolas called Irala to him.

"You'll be in charge of the settlement and the ships," Ayolas said. "In effect then, you'll be governor until my return. All I want you to do is to stay here and wait for me. I don't think the Indians will attack you; but you can, if attacked, defend yourselves. I will be back, and then, we shall all be rich."

The haunting legend of *El Dorado* had inflamed the minds of many men before Ayolas. It was said to be a land of glitter, where a gilded white man lived. This king annointed his body each day with liquid gold; and each night, he washed himself clean of it. The gold that fell from him each year would buy half of Spain. But where did he come from, this fabulous king, and where was the land he ruled? The Indian guide spoke of high mountains and wide plains that they would have to traverse, leaving their vessel which was anchored in the river.

Ayolas did not live to see the land he longed for, which many historians now feel must have been Peru. On the way, in company with his brave men, he met death at the hands of the Indians. Whether he was killed by natives who wanted to prevent him from seeing the golden kingdom, or whether his death came senselessly, no one knows.

After a time Irala grew tired of waiting for Ayolas. There was a whole country, a continent, to explore. Perhaps he was the one to find *El Dorado*, not Ayolas. On June 23, 1537, Irala sailed two luggers up the Paraná River to the Paraguay, and then up the Paraguay. He and his companions watched the shore, amazed at the lushness and beauty of the countryside. The desolate prairie was nowhere to be seen. Instead a shining green jungle seemed to move with a mysterious life of its own, sprinkled with tropical flowers, a sword's length across. Unseen creatures stirred the foliage and uttered strange cries; colorful birds moved noisily through the air. Further on, on clear stretches of land, Guaranís were planting corn. This was a land with a future.

It was in this lush paradise that Irala decided to establish a settlement. It was from here, from this peaceful and beautiful country, that he would continue his search for gold. But first he and his men would build a home, a place to come back to. They would build a city in the middle of the jungle. Among other things, this would prove to the natives that the Spanish could tame anything and had taken possession of everything, including the wilderness.

It was important to choose the right site, not one exposed like Buenos Aires—one sheltered by nature, yet one that gave a broad view of the lands around. Irala chose a high bluff, overlooking the river and acres of green jungle. Indian slaves, Irala promised, would carve into that jungle and cultivate gardens and fields.

"It is from here we shall rule," Irala proclaimed.

Santa María de Asunción was a city planted, rather than built. It was planted like a seed of faith or a seed of hate can be planted in a man. Yet it was a primitively beautiful residential town and stockaded fort. The local Indians were at first asked to help, then forced to help build it, as a prelude to other work that would be demanded of them.

Within a year Asunción assumed its character, a self-indulgent, imperious, unscrupulous settlement, yet one which inspired admiration for the very fact of its existence.

Irala was elected governor by his companions, pending a royal appointment. The settlers were glad it was Irala who was their leader. They admired him, for they felt that everything he did he did for their welfare. From the start, from the time the first stone was laid in Asunción, he had assured them that they were in a land of plenty, that they would profit from its riches, and they would not have to labor. They would be, he promised them, the aristocracy of a new continent. They and their children and their grandchildren would live well; and the Indians, either willingly or enslaved, would work for them to make them ever richer. These promises were kept, for those who had come with him to Asunción and for the survivors of Buenos Aires, who came to join them, after the supply ships finally arrived from Spain in 1538.

13

In 1541 Cabeza de Vaca's expedition reached South America. To see the lands over which he would rule, to meet the natives he had come to protect, to once again breathe the air of the unknown, to stretch his legs, he decided to walk to Asunción.

"He is mad," some of his men said.

"He's been mad ever since the Nárvez expedition to Florida. He's been a madman for fourteen years, and he's supposed to lead us!"

"He'll lead us to certain death."

It was amidst such grumbling that Cabeza de Vaca announced that he was taking 250 men with him.

"You'll grow accustomed to nature," he told them. "You'll grow to love it and not to fear it. And by walking through this land, we will meet many natives. We will make friends with them. That will be the most important benefit we will reap."

The rest of his expedition sailed on to Asunción. When Irala saw the ships approach, he was ready to meet Cabeza de Vaca and acknowledge him as governor, something many of his comrades were totally unwilling to do. But Irala felt that a royal order should not be disobeyed. As long as Alvar Núñez Cabeza de Vaca was governor, Irala would obey. But he, as everyone else, hoped that it would not be for long. A petition had already gone from the colonists to the King, begging His Majesty to officially appoint Irala as governor.

It was not Cabeza de Vaca who came down the gangplank, however. It was a young officer. Irala thought, at once, that the governor was sick. His friends were hoping he had died.

"Alvar Núñez," the officer said, bowing to Irala, "the governor of His Majesty, has chosen to come to Asunción by land."

Irala only smiled, for he was still a man of restraint where social graces were concerned. But his companions, to whom etiquette was a lost art, burst into laughter.

"Cabeza de Vaca will never reach us," they said.

"I hope the Guaranís will like him."

"I hear he is a skinny man."

"Then, the Guaranís will not like him!"

"Well, thank God, Irala is still our governor."

"Nothing has changed."

But things were changing. A man was taking four months and nine days to walk across a wilderness. During that time he was forming his policies toward the natives. And he was talking to the natives and hearing their grievances.

"We shall barter with them," he informed his men. "Trading will be the way of life. If we want provisions from them, we will repay them immediately with whatever they need that is of equal value. If we want the Indians to work for us, we will give them adequate compensation for that work. There will be no slavery in South America, only willing labor, paid labor."

The men snickered among themselves. They had heard stories of the easy life in Asunción. Had they come to play nursemaid to the heathen? And how could they get rich if they were going to pay for everything?

"He is a fanatic," someone declared. "Look at his eyes. All you have to do is look at his eyes. They burn with an inner fire."

"He is a madman."

"No, he is a fanatic. There is a difference. A madman has no mission in life; a fanatic lives only for whatever mission he feels he has. Fanatics are more dangerous than madmen. And this fanatic has the power to destroy us all."

"Can you imagine such a thing? He wants to protect the Indians, yet he was enslaved by the Indians for years. Wouldn't you think a Spaniard would seek revenge on his torturers?"

"Our only hope is Irala. He is a true leader. He cares for the colonists and not for the heathen."

And they began to look with hatred at the white-haired man who led them through wilderness. He looked like some maddened prophet from the Old Testament and not at all like a conquistador.

The closer the new governor and his men came to Asunción the more complaints there were from the Indians. They came in groups, slowing the journey, with tales of ill treatment, of injustices, of forced labor, of the taking of mothers from children and husbands from wives. As the accounts of brutalities committed by the colonists came in, the blame was always put squarely on Irala. It was he who was the leader of the colonists; it was his example that the others followed; and it was he who was the most cruel and the most ruthless of the exploiters, the Indians reasoned.

So Cabeza de Vaca was convinced, before he reached the city in the jungle, that his adversary was one, and his name was Irala.

14

The runner breathed heavily, his powerful chest heaving, his muscular brown legs shiny with sweat; sweat also ran down his forehead and cheeks and caught in the hollow between his neck and shoulders. He was a young Spanish soldier, and this had been his first important mission. As a reward, he had been promised an Indian slave.

"The Governor will be in Asunción within two hours." He said it all in one breath, as if to prove to the men gathered around Irala that not all of his strength had been sapped by the speed at which he had run five miles.

Irala smiled at the unhappy expressions on the faces of his friends.

"Did you really think," he asked "that Cabeza de Vaca would not make it? After all he is the man who walked across a continent, from one sea to another."

"What was he trying to prove?" one of Asunción's settlers asked, scratching his head. "That he is as mad as they say he is, or as fearless as he thinks himself?"

"Whatever his reasons," still another shouted, "he should be denounced to the Council of the Indies. It is a crime to risk Spanish lives on such a trek."

"How many men did he lose?" Irala asked the runner.

"Only two," the runner replied, lifting two fingers up, a habit he had acquired from talking to the natives. "And those two," he added, for there was silence in the room, "died of natural causes. One drowned and the other just dropped dead. His heart stopped beating."

"What else did you find out?" Irala's voice sounded impatient.

"Many Indians came to him with complaints."

"And what did he tell them?"

'He swore to them that they will be protected by him and by God."

"Protected from what?" one of the men exclaimed.

The runner was going to answer, but Irala raised his hand. "From us, from the Spaniards, of course. He is, after all," he told them, "a fanatic as far as the Indians are concerned. I have heard that he wants them, not the Spanish, to rule the world."

"But what will we do about this madman?"

"We'll let him see that he cannot conquer us."

Two hours later Irala, along with the Spanish settlers and a multitude of native servants, bowed to the new governor. Irala knelt and received from Cabeza de Vaca's hand the King's Ordinance. Then, with his head still bowed but a sharp smile on his lips, he swore allegiance to the new governor in his own name and in the name of all those who lived in Paraguay.

In Santo Domingo, Cabeza de Vaca had seen Spanish settlers trying to duplicate in the tropics life as they had lived it in Spain. But Asunción was not at all like the Caribbean. Here there was a bigger price to be paid for living surrounded by wilderness. The conquerors looked as savage as the conquered. The Spaniards' beards were long; their tattered clothes were barely a cover for the toughened skins of their bodies. Some had already discarded their last shreds of Spanish dress and wore deerskins or trousers of native cotton; but regardless of what he wore, each one seemed to hold on to a piece of silk or brocade, as if the luxury of even a fragment of material could assure them of always remaining Spanish *caballeros*.

Much as they wished to remain aristocrats, however, they had long since shed the manners of gentlemen. They laughed loudly and spoke uncouthly. They wiped their noses on their hands and spat freely. There was something in their diet that made their teeth rot; and most of them, with their blackened teeth, their wild beards and bloodshot eyes, would have scared Spanish children, even their own children, far more than the local Indians.

In comparison, the Guaranís, who were everywhere, were a handsome people. They were rather short of stature. Their coarse hair shone with a blue-black light. Their round cheeks were complimented by short foreheads and broad chins. Their eyes, slanting obliquely, were shaded by amazingly thick and curly eyelashes. Their full mouths and strong jaws contrasted sharply with their noses, which were short, thin and generally upturned. These noses, white teeth, a warmly colored skin, butter yellow with a tint of red, and low voices, made the Guaranís pleasing to both eye and ear.

Since the natives, prior to the arrival of the Spaniards, suffered from nothing more serious than goiter, there was no local sickness. With the variety of tropical vegetation, the food was plentiful. Beans, corn, pumpkins, peanuts, and yams were cultivated for both the settlers and the natives. The Indians also provided ample game. But above and beyond fish and game, fruits and vegetables, the natives considered human flesh to be the greatest of delicacies.

Cabeza de Vaca got up early his first morning in Asunción and walked the streets of the town to find out for himself how the inhabitants lived. He saw the straw-thatched, wooden cabins that belonged to the Spanish gentry and the adobe huts where the Indian servants lived. The biggest of the cabins belonged to Irala, but even it looked humble. In the marketplace Cabeza de Vaca saw Indian women, with tatooed breasts, selling their wares; woven blankets and beautifully shaped and gaily painted pottery.

"Do they believe in some gods?" Cabeza de Vaca asked a man, the only Spaniard in the marketplace.

"Not really. Not the Guaranís." The man looked more closely at Cabeza de Vaca. "You are the new governor. I thought you'd be the last one up. Spanish gentlemen don't wake up before noon around here. You should be interested in the Spanish gods, not the Indians. We're getting fat with inactivity; and we have begun to worship laziness and gluttony and all the other vices."

"Much bad blood is brewing around here. Some men have more than others. Each man grabs what he can, and nothing is done in the light of justice or law. Many have debts as large as if they were living in Spain. Others have only one ambition, to own more slaves than anyone else. But having these slaves, since few owners know what to do with them, is not doing anyone any good."

The man began to walk, and Cabeza de Vaca walked with him. They reached a long hut, and the man opened the door. Inside was an oblong table that stretched from the front door to the back, taking most of the room. On the patio, beyond the long room, stood a press and other machine-like objects.

"What is this?" Cabeza de Vaca asked, looking around with curiosity.

"It's my shop," the man said. "My name is Domingo Martínez. Some time ago I decided that I ought to start working for a living, and since then I have become a rare item, a businessman, the only one in Asunción. If you come over here, Governor, I'll show you what we manufacture."

Martínez showed Cabeza de Vaca his inventions: a machine that stamped out fish hooks, a silversmith bellows, and a press that crushed sugar cane.

"What you are doing is admirable," said Cabeza de Vaca, after he found out that Martínez paid the Indians for their work.

"How about taxes?" he asked. "Have they been collected all along?"

Martínez laughed.

"Yes, we've got tax collectors. They keep every fifth deer and every fifth fish for the Crown." He laughed again. "You just came from Spain. Did you ever see any slightly rotten fish or deer from these parts?"

Their conversation was interrupted by the arrival of a dozen Indian workers. Martínez greeted them all by name, and Cabeza de Vaca was happy to see that they looked at the Spaniard with respect and not a trace of fear. When their work was organized, Cabeza de Vaca asked Martínez about the Indians and their treatment.

"We did not introduce slavery here. It existed before we came. The Guaranís made slaves of their captured enemies. Now they themselves live a life of servitude. They are not paid by the Spaniards and are often whipped by the masters, if not for disciplinary reasons, then for a whim. Strangely enough, they were happy to see us when we first arrived. They offered us their daughters for wives and all their worldly possessions as gestures of friendship. Unfortunately, we were not satisfied with what we were given. We took what they didn't give us. . . ."

"What about Irala? Didn't he exercise any authority? Didn't he forbid excesses; didn't he want to keep the friendship of the natives?"

Once again the man laughed.

"Irala is and always has been the leader of all who are greedy. He is the very worst offender."

"I hope I did not come too late . . ."

"What can you do?"

"As Governor I can . . ."

Martínez put his hand out.

"If you take the slaves from the soldiers, you'll turn them against you. If you try to reform the settlers, you'll risk an uprising or a knifing in your own bed. There are some facts you should remember: these people have carved a city out of the wilderness; they have declared themselves absolute masters; and not one of them considers you Governor of Asunción. Irala was and always will be the leader of these people. If you are his friend, they'll listen to you; if you are not, they will ignore you at best, and hate you, or kill you, at worst."

As he walked away from Domingo Martínez, Cabeza de Vaca was not worried about his own authority or that of Irala. He saw the question of authority as a simple one. The people would have to obey the King's Governor; the question was what should be done? It was obvious that the exploitation of the natives must stop and stop immediately.

That same afternoon he called a meeting of everyone in town, including all the clergy. Here he intended to present a plea for a Christian decision to treat the natives as fellow human beings, with compassion and love. The meeting was held in the square of the town, overlooking the brown waters of the Paraguay River.

Before he spoke, Cabeza de Vaca looked intently into the faces of the settlers; the hard faces, the proud faces, the challenging faces of those who did not intend to be his friends and dared him to govern them. The smile of mockery on Irala's face was an encouragement to others; and suddenly, the entire crowd seemed to smile at him, and there was neither joy nor kindness in any of those smiles.

"My friends," he began. His voice sounded strong to him, yet, in his throat he felt the dryness of fear. "Fellow Christians. Once, a long time ago, before I started off on the expedition with Nárvaez, I talked with Father Las Casas. At that time I cared little about natives of any land. I was brought up in my grandfather's house, where he had kept many slaves from the Canaries . . ." They kept smiling at him, as if they were not hearing a word.

"Father Las Casas," he continued, "said one thing which I shall never forget. I remembered his words in Santo Domingo, as I heard there of mass suicides by natives; I remembered his words in the land of Florida, when I was myself made a slave; I remembered his words as I lived for years among primitive tribes. Father Las Casas told me to see Christ's face in every Indian's face. And I did; and seeing it, I could not want to hurt any of them."

The people were no longer smiling. Their faces had become hard.

"He blasphemes!" someone cried, but no one else took it up. For a second, Cabeza de Vaca thought he had imagined the shout, for there was no movement, no change of facial expression anywhere. They do not want, they even refuse, to understand, he thought. Now he was angry. If he could not convince them by words, then he would give commands.

"From this day on," his voice was much louder now, and there was wrath just below its surface, "any ill treatment of the natives will be reported directly to me. I will hear such reports from anyone, including the natives themselves. If I hear of anyone mistreating an Indian, I will take the Indian away from that person and give him to a more charitable one. Since slavery exists openly, it will eventually be abolished openly. But I shall make

135

no hasty decisions; I'll give all of you time, a few months, to realize that to enslave a human being is wrong. And to mistreat another is to sin again God's commandments. I hope most sincerely that you will relinquish your slaves voluntarily. Tomorrow I shall appoint a priest and an interpreter to hear all complaints brought to me by the Indians."

A murmuring swept like the wind through the tree tops. He could distinguish such words as *madman, traitor, Indian-lover* and *heathen-worshipper*. He realized, then that each man present was his enemy. It was not only Irala he had to fight. It was all of them. His own face was now as hard as theirs.

"And I want," his voice was cold, "to make it clear to all of you that these are not my orders alone. If you disobey them, you will be disobeying the Royal Patent, which makes slavery illegal."

With that, he turned his back on them. Among the men who had listened to him, there were three emotions: anger, resentment, and hatred. And of the three, the last was strongest and more lasting.

Cabeza de Vaca was well aware of the climate of hate around him. Wherever he went, he heard derisive laughter. It was either that, laughter, or silence that greeted him. He was an outcast; he lived the life of a hermit in his Governor's house. His only distraction from work was the daily Mass. But finally one day he sought out Domingo Martínez.

"The fish hooks are coming out all wrong," Martínez said in answer to the Governor's greeting, his head bent over his machine. Cabeza de Vaca wondered if his presence in the man's shop might hurt his business. "It's like some of your laws."

"Which laws?" He was grateful that Martínez now looked up with neither hatred nor resentment nor anger in his face.

"You forbade the Spaniards to buy Indians taken by the Guaranís in tribal warfare, didn't you?"

"Yes."

"Do you know what the Guaranís do with them, with the captives that no longer have any value?"

"No, I don't."

"They eat them."

Cabeza de Vaca caught his breath. He had never guessed that one of his laws was directly responsible for the continuation of cannibalism.

"All sorts of laws have side effects," Martínez said gently. "And still we must have them. Did anyone tell you, before you were sent here, that the most important thing a governor must do is to keep closing his eyes?" Martínez laughed. "But of course if you could do that you would not be the man you are, and they probably would not have sent you here."

These were the first kind words Cabeza de Vaca had heard since the last time he had spoken to Martínez. This man, who understood him, could help him. He did not want to compromise on the issue of freedom for the Indians, but maybe he could do something else constructive that would help the colonists. He did want friends.

"What do they resent most of all?" he asked.

"What they think is favoritism. They didn't appreciate it when in one breath you forbade the Spaniards to leave the city without permission or to step outside of its walls after nightfall, and in the next breath you granted the natives the right to visit relatives whenever they chose."

"But you know why I did that!" Cabeza de Vaca saw in the man's face that he did understand: it was to prevent the Spaniards from capturing new slaves and to give the Indians a sense of freedom. "I see," he said looking at Martínez, who had been waiting for him to speak, "that they could misunderstand. It might seem to them that I was denying freedom to one group in order to give some of it to another. And freedom does not need such rationing."

Martínez smiled. He had liked Cabeza de Vaca from the very first. This was the kind of man that he had always admired: a courageous man, a man without price, a man unafraid to stand alone.

"I will not," Cabeza de Vaca began, and he hurried on as if his thoughts were crowding him, "punish anyone for offenses committed before I came here. I will postpone payment of debts until we find the treasure of *El Dorado*. I will send out an expedition to find that treasure; and Irala, who I will name my adjutant and first lieutenant, will lead it."

Hurriedly he shook the hand of Domingo Martínez, grateful for an insight into the harm he was doing. To foster hatred was as bad a sin as to keep one's eyes closed to injustice and dishonesty. There must be a middle ground, he thought; and he would find it.

For a few weeks he worked hard, trying to soothe the feelings of the colonists. But no sooner had he gained some supporters with his new tactics, than he lost them over three separate incidents. The first involved Cabrera, a close friend of Irala who had been the Crown's chief tax collector. Examining his records, Cabeza de Vaca found such blatant dishonesty that he heatedly spoke of beheading the man. Then, second, he fired another friend of Irala, the most popular man among the settlers, notary Martín de Orue, and replaced him with Pedro Hernandez. Hernandez had never been a bureaucrat, and so he failed to preface the Governor's orders with the customary "los señores oficiales." By this omission, he gave offence to the prideful founders of Asunción. The third incident took place when Cabeza de Vaca, as chief justice, presided over the case of a native girl called Juliana, accused of poisoning her Christian husband. The evidence against her was overwhelming, and the girl herself freely admitted the murder. Cabeza de Vaca condemned her to death. No sooner had he pronounced the sentence than Irala's voice was heard from the back of the courtroom.

"A friend of mine has taken a fancy to the girl. I'd like to buy her for him."

Cabeza de Vaca was outraged by Irala's request. In full view of a courtroom filled with Irala's friends, he spat out his disgust and shouted out his anger and indignation.

With the scene in the courtroom, the truce between Cabeza de Vaca and the settlers, if there had been a truce, was over. And he knew it. What could he do next? He spent many sleepless nights searching his mind. He had never wanted to buy the people's allegiance, but he had tried to be easy with them; he had even gone so far as to make justice work on a part time basis. Finally, exhausted by the struggle, and after hours of prayer, he would still lie sleepless. Then he would think of the years he had spent in North America. Those years of slavery and of searching and wandering, seemed now to have been the happiest years of his life.

The Governor's attention was drawn away from his problems at Asunción by reports of trouble between the Indians. The Guaycurúes were molesting the Guaranís and since the latter were vassals of His Majesty, they were entitled to protection. The Guaranís killed their enemies with their deadly *boleadors*, and the Guaycurúes decapitated theirs.

Cabeza de Vaca officially declared war on the invaders and sent four dozen Spaniards with an ultimatum to the Guaycurúes, either to surrender or to expect total war. The envoys were greeted with a barrage of arrows, which the Guaycurúes used when the enemy was out of hand-reach. Total war it would be.

Many of the settlers had believed that Cabeza de Vaca would never use force against the Indians. They soon saw how wrong they had been. Cabeza de Vaca himself led an army of 200 infantry men, 12 cavalry men, and a sizeable number of Guaranís. To distinguish them from the enemy, the Guaranís had their breasts and backs painted with large crosses.

The night before the planned attack, when even the insects seemed to have stopped humming and the heavy breath of the tropic air made men groggy in their sleep, a sudden commotion in the camp panicked Pedro Hernandez, a light sleeper. Thinking that the Guaranís were revolting, he fired point-blank into the darkness. Two of his bullets grazed Cabeza de Vaca's face. He had not been asleep and had risen to go among the Guaranís to find out the reason for the sudden noise. His face bleeding, the Governor leaped from his horse and followed the fleeing and frightened Indians. He pleaded with them until he convinced them that they had nothing to fear, that the incident was an accident.

Early the next morning, amid shouts of *Santiago* the attack was launched. The Guaycurúes were not prepared for the enthusiasm with which the Guaranís and the Spanish took to battle. Most of them fled, first setting fire to their straw houses; but a few fought back, killing two Spaniards and twelve Guaranís.

Returning to Asunción victorious, with four hundred prisoners, Cabeza de Vaca found the settlers ready to forget and to forgive. But only for a while. Hatred came back with the Governor's announcement that the prisoners would not be made slaves. Instead, a messenger was dispatched to the chief of the tribe, and peace was cemented by the return of the prisoners and an exchange of gifts.

Once again, Cabeza de Vaca lived the life of a hermit in Asuncíon. But he soon found that he did have friends. The Guaranís were grateful to him for taking their part in the war and for begging them to forgive the incident on the eve of the battle; the Guaycurúes loved him for freeing their prisoners. A bond united the Governor with the natives, a bond that at the same time separated him further from the settlers.

He loved to get up early in the morning and walk to the river's edge. The Guaycurúes, now at peace, became the tribe that provided the city with most of its necessities. Cabeza de Vaca discovered that they were a fun-loving people, who delighted in playing practical jokes on one another.

Cabeza de Vaca knew that he was expected to explore relentlessly until he found the legendary *El Dorado*.

Not only were the settlers waiting for new riches, but the Crown was impatient.

"How will you go about searching for *El Dorado?*" Martínez asked Cabeza de Vaca one day when the Governor stopped by.

"I know," Cabeza de Vaca said, "that we must have the help and the co-operation of the Indians. Without them, without their friendship, we will be defeated as the others have been. This is their land; *El Dorado* is also theirs. If we want to share in it, we must share it with the Indians. I am going to call a meeting of all the Indian chiefs and ask for their help. I'll tell them why it is necessary for us to find *El Dorado*. I'll be frank with them. If we are united, we will not fail in the search for gold or in anything else."

"All of this sounds fine," Martínez said, "but watch out for Indian treachery. They are not like us, and neither are we like them. There is a great gulf between peoples, the gulf of civilization, custom, religion. We, too, are treacherous, and we should warn the Indians against our brand of treachery. But I am warning you against them. Especially against Aracaré."

The chief called Aracaré, when approached, was the strongest supporter of the Spanish desire to find and explore *El Dorado*. He assured and reassured Cabeza de Vaca that the help of his entire tribe and tribes friendly to him were at the disposal of the Spanish.

On October 20, 1542, Irala, with three luggers, ninety Spaniards, and numerous Indian chieftains, set sail up the Paraguay River to find an inland trail to the west, to the kingdom of the gilded man.

This was Irala's fifth journey up the river; but this

time he was sailing with the Indians, not against them, trusting them, in effect, protected by them. Betrayal came swiftly and unexpectedly. And it was Aracaré who was the betrayer. He ordered the tribes who lived along the banks of the river to set their fields on fire, a sign of war. Many of Irala's expedition, both Spanish and Indian, turned back, frightened by this open hostility. But Irala did not. He continued inland and traversed 250 leagues.

Receiving word of the treachery, Cabeza de Vaca issued an order for the execution of Aracaré. The order was carried out, and the Guaranís, through whose lands Irala was traveling suddenly turned against him. Atabaré, the brother of the executed chieftain, pursued Irala, swearing to avenge his brother or die himself in the process. But Irala escaped and on February 11 was safely back in Asunción. He told his friends that the expedition would have been a success had it not been for the foolish order of Cabeza de Vaca to execute Aracaré.

During his absence, a great fire had burned down the city of Asunción, its thatched huts inflamed further by 7,000 bushels of Indian corn. Before Irala's return, Cabeza de Vaca replaced all the dwellings with solidly built houses of clay and encircled the city with a wall of tree trunks, driven deeply into the ground. He had also helped, with his own hands, to build a new church, Our Lady of September, and a central plaza. The rebuilding of Asunción was done according to the medieval custom, all inhabitants participating in the physical labor. The Governor had hoped that this undertaking would bring him closer to the settlers. With Irala's return, the uneasy truce he had begun was once again broken.

During his report to the Governor, Irala contended that he himself would never have executed Aracaré.

"But can't you see," Cabeza de Vaca said earnestly, "he had committed the crime of treason. Had he been a Spaniard, he would have had to die for it."

"I rather thought," Irala said, his usual smile curving his lips, "that this was your way of showing the settlers that you are on their side."

"You thought," Cabeza de Vaca exclaimed, "that I was trying to buy the settlers?"

Irala did not answer.

"It was the only just thing to do," Cabeza de Vaca said. "And justice should not know color or creed."

"The Spaniards misunderstood your motives," Irala said. "They think you as bloodthirsty and cruel as the best of them."

Cabeza de Vaca looked at Irala uncomprehendingly. How can it be, he thought, that I am so grossly misunderstood? Why is it that I cannot reach these people, my people? And I have also lost contact with the Indians.

After the meeting Cabeza de Vaca locked himself in his room. Were his ideas wrong? What if he had been wrong, wrong all along: wrong in treating the Indians the way he had; wrong in treating the settlers the way he had; wrong in peace, and wrong in war? Maybe his ideas of justice were not meant for the wilderness; maybe it was he who must change. All this time he had been certain of what was right and what was wrong. Now, he was certain of just one thing: he was a total failure, as a governor and as a man. Yet as he thought on, his conscience denied this, and his honesty forbade him to believe that principles were expendable.

But the feeling of personal failure persisted. And because of this, he let Irala lead the expedition against Atabaré. And it was Irala, and not he, who, with 250 men sudued the rebellious Indians and came back to Asunción with the enemy bent and begging for peace. Throughout a long summer and while this was being done, Cabeza de Vaca struggled with himself and was aware of the popular sentiment. The people liked and admired Irala, and they hated and despised everything Cabeza de Vaca stood for.

By mid-winter he had made an important decision. He would lead the expedition to *El Dorado* himself and he would take with him all the troublemakers, all those who hated him most. He would leave behind those who had come with him from Spain and were still, if not his friends, not yet his enemies, to guard Asunción. He was hoping that the more hardened settlers would discover something in the hardships of jungle travel that would soften their spirits and turn their minds away from pettiness and spite.

The day for journeying came, September 8, 1543. The expedition consisted of 10 luggers, 400 Spaniards, 10 horses, and 1200 Guaranís in 120 canoes. They were plentifully supplied with food and gifts for the natives. The countryside, as they sailed up the river, was unbelievably beautiful, lush with colors during the brilliance of day and loud with sounds of life at night. Whenever Cabeza de Vaca saw an Indian settlement, he went ashore and talked to the natives.

"Are we after gold or Indians' love?" the men began to murmur.

The journey, because of the stops, was slow; and it

was more than a month before they reached the site of Candelaría. It was from there, six years before that Ayolas had left in search of gold.

Beyond Candelaría, the expedition sailed through a much different type of country. Instead of a Garden of Eden, they were now in a region of marshes, lakes, and the treacherously swirling currents of an uncharted river. The animals and birds were noisy and terrifyingly numerous. Monkeys competed with parrots in cutting the air with shrieks of blood-curdling suddenness. Deer jumped high in the air, fleeing the men, or stood motionless as if hypnotized by the expedition. Lizards bumped into crocodiles and crocodiles pushed aside armadillos. Opossums and anteaters seemed to be struggling for possession of dry land.

The men saw anthills, higher than a man on a horse. From the local Indians they learned of the perils of this land. There were wasps that, with a sting, could paralyze a man. Vampire bats ruled the land at night with their taste for the blood of living creatures. And quicksand lay, as if in wait, in the way of those trying to escape any and all of the jungle horrors.

On November 8, they arrived at Puerto de los Reyes, the furthest point reached by Irala on the previous expedition. The Governor went immediately to the natives and implored them to receive the faith of Christ and Spain's sovereignty. He was so persuasive that within hours bonfires burning wooden idols lit the sky. He promised the natives that a church would be built and a priest as well as some white men would stay with them. He planted a great cross on the river's shore, a cross that cast a shadow at night on the treacherous waters.

The natives were promptly nicknamed Orejones (great ears) by the Spaniards, for their ears were enlarged to a dozen times their ordinary size. They were pierced at an early age, and wooden disks, heavier and bigger each year, or gourds, were inserted in them. With time the ears hung down a long way, terribly large and to the Spanish amusingly ugly. Whenever the Indians did work that required bending down, or when they were at war, they tied their ears behind their heads or even rolled them up as one would a carpet.

Because of their appearance, most of the Spaniards laughed at them, but Cabeza de Vaca, after his first day's success, became fast friends with the Orejones.

While the church was being built at Los Reyes, several small expeditions were sent further on, but they all came back with reports of flood. They also brought back rumors of gold nearby and of a tribe of warlike women, the Amazons.

"The rainy season will last another two months," the natives told Cabeza de Vaca.

"Your soldiers are growing restless," Irala said. "And the settlers feel dissatisfied with this fruitless search and enforced inactivity."

"We shall vote, then," Cabeza de Vaca announced, "vote whether to stay here and wait for the rains to cease and then continue on, or to go back to Asunción. But remember that we have plenty of provisions left; and when they are used up, this land will yield enough food for everyone. So do not let the fear of hunger color your decision."

The majority voted to sail back.

15

In spite of the vote and in spite of the desire of the majority to return to Asunción immediately, Cabeza de Vaca delayed that return. He was obsessed with the idea that this land, this outpost in the wilderness, must test the strength and the spirit of Christianity and Spanish civilization. This he planned to accomplish through the dispensation of justice. For it was only on a foundation of freedom and justice for all, he reasoned, that any Christian country could exist.

None of the Spanish even tried to understand his viewpoint. They had all given up, if they had ever tried. And if none quite dared to promote open rebellion, many did not hesitate to sow further the seeds of hate.

Cáceres and Irala did not openly encourage underhanded tactics, yet many of their friends took it upon themselves "as members of the opposition" to inflame hatred and speed up an open revolt among the soldiers. They hoped for a mutiny against Cabeza de Vaca; and they did not hesitate to use any covert means they could to bring it about.

"That one's too drunk to understand," a friend of Cáceres said pointing to a soldier.

"A few of them got into some Spanish brandy," the man with him said. "I'll bet this is the first time for him."

"Let's go," the first man said.

"No. We've got a job to do."

The two men approached the young soldier, and he opened his eyes to the touch of their hands on his shoulders. They shook him, and for a minute he did not know where he was.

"The Governor is talking of hanging you," one of the men said loudly. The soldier thought he had imagined the words, yet the man repeated it, and added: "He called you a traitor."

And now the other man's voice, even louder, boomed into his ear, splitting his head in two.

"The Governor is very angry with you. He's angry because you spied on him. But both Irala and Cáceres came forth in your defence. Remember, if it were not for them, you'd be hanged instead of drunk tonight."

It was in the midst of intrigue of this kind, that Cabeza de Vaca was crying for justice. To implement it, he called a meeting of the nearby Indian chiefs. He called them together that he might hear any complaints they had against the Spanish, complaints held over from previous visits of the white men to the area.

149

"Once, a long time ago," an elderly soldier said, as the men watched the Indian chieftains arrive by canoe, "the Christians were thrown to the lions in Rome's colliseum. Today Cabeza de Vaca will throw the Christians to the Indians."

All that day Cabeza de Vaca sat listening to complaints. He had felt the first symptoms of fever in the morning when he got up. The early morning air had made him shiver with cold, and suddenly the same air had bathed him in sweat. His brain seemed ready to explode; it felt as if it had expanded like a balloon, and his skull could not contain it. Yet, while his forehead burned, his eyes hurt, and shivers raked his body, he listened and listened to the Indian chiefs. And when they fell silent, he didn't seem to be satisfied with the remembered wrongs; he tried to bring back memories of forgotten hurts by asking questions. And when evening came and Cabeza de Vaca's fevered eyes could not distinguish light from dark, he promised the Indians to punish the guilty and compensate those who had suffered loss or injury.

That same night another meeting was held, this one without Cabeza de Vaca, and a verdict was reached:

"There is no other way. He must die."

They discussed until morning how best to bring about that death. Hungry, tired, and hot, they finally agreed that they would make it look like an accident. No one wanted to be blamed for the Governor's death, and no one would be. An alarm would be sounded, as if there had been an unexpected attack by the Indians. In the confusion, a shot would be fired, and a bullet would find Cabeza de Vaca's head. This terrible accident would then be immediately reported to the Crown and to the Council of Indian Affairs, with a detailed description of the night of confusion, confusion that was directly responsible for the tragic death of the Governor.

The young soldier, who the night before had gotten drunk for the first time in his life, heard the plan, and more in fear for his soul than out of a sense of duty, went to the Governor's tent.

"I have come to warn you, sir," he whispered. "They have decided to kill you."

The Governor lay silent, his eyes shining much too brightly in the dim light of the misty dawn. A wave of heat seemed to rise from his body, and from the crumpled coat on which he had slept. He looked more dead than alive.

"Who?" the Governor whispered. "Who will have me dead?"

"Irala," the young soldier said, and with that he fled.

Cabeza de Vaca lay breathing heavily after the soldier had left. He was gathering strength. It was a long way to the clearing where he had held the meeting that day. There were over a hundred feet between him and the bench on which he had sat, listening to the Indians. But he intended to get to it before the others awoke, even if he had to crawl on his hands and knees. And get to it, he did.

Two hours later, when the sun had reached the top of the lower trees, the Governor was seated on the wooden bench and his notary, Pedro Hernandez, was beside him.

"I want a formal indictment against Irala drawn up," Cabeza de Vaca said, measuring each word with the strength left in him.

"What for?"

"For being the instigator of a mutiny," Cabeza de Vaca said. "Call a meeting," he added with the last of his strength, "and have the indictment read to all."

He sat up straight during the hearing, praying that he would not collapse in front of them. He sat straight, his back against the wooden bench even when he could no longer distinguish words from hallucinations. When he was given a pen to sign the document, he desperately tried to hold it, but his hand shook with a fever that could no longer be controlled by willpower.

After that he never knew what was nightmare and what was reality. He was unconscious during an attack by a hostile group of the Guaranís. They came at night and killed a dozen Spaniards. In his delirium, he tried to give orders. "Don't show them any mercy," some heard him say. "Teach them a lesson! Chastise them until they understand justice."

And that is what the Spanish did. For Cabeza de Vaca it was a long night of screams, frightening visions, and finally quiet, interrupted only by soft words and shadows. But for the Spanish it was a night of great victory.

"No one knows, no one knows how many were killed."

"But we took more than two thousand prisoners."

With morning the fever receded enough for him to give orders. They were to break camp and start back to Asunción. This was enough to make men cheer outside his tent. He called Pedro Hernandez to him.

"Before we leave each man must give up his Indian

woman," he said, "The women must be taken back to their families."

As this order was repeated, the cheering stopped and was replaced by murmurings. It was the same ominous sound he had heard so often in Asunción.

It was March 24, 1544, when the luggers followed by the canoes left Puerto de los Reyes. Carbeza de Vaca gave the order to lift anchor, the very last order he was ever to give, and he waved goodby to his Indian friends. Then as suddenly as the fever had left him, it came back; and he was delirious all the way back to Asunción.

During his rare moments of consciousness, Cabeza de Vaca had premonitions of disaster. He had led his enemies in search of riches, and he had failed. They had all seen his failure. In his nightmares he saw the mocking smile that was always on Irala's lips, on the lips of all those sailing back to Asunción.

But very few smiled on that trip. The Governor was not the only man gripped by the fever, most of the others lay ill, too, during the fifteen-day journey. As they sailed, from the shores came waves of arrows, or sometimes a single Indian would bend his bow and fire his weapon at them. The men did nothing; they were either too sick to fight back or too anxious to return to their homes. The expedition landed in Asunción at dawn on April 8.

Cabeza de Vaca's illness continued long after everyone else's had ended. He was much too weak, even when the fever passed, to resume his duties as governor. The conspirators plotted in earnest and openly now. Domingo Martínez, his only friend among the settlers, would often come to the Governor's bedside.

"Juan de Salazar," Martínez would say, unwilling to report on the progress of the conspiracy for fear his friend was too feeble to hear the worst, "has almost finished building ships that will soon sail for Spain."

"What of the Indians?" the governor would ask.

"The Agaces are in rebellion again."

The Governor would try to get up, but would fall weakly against the pillows.

But the day came when Domingo Martínez and a handful of Cabeza de Vaca's friends, men who had come with him from Spain, decided to tell the Governor the truth.

"The entire city is against you."

"They have spread so many lies, so many accusations that now everyone, from the common soldiers to the priests, believe that you are mad. They believe that you'll deprive them of all they have acquired, that you will give even the land back to the natives."

"They say that when you are able to get up, you'll be harder on them than ever."

"Who are my worst enemies?" Cabeza de Vaca asked feebly.

"Irala, of course, and Cáceres and Alonso Cabrera and Garcí-Vanegas, Francisco de Mendoza, Pedro Dorantes . . ."

They were all names of men who had been on the expedition with him.

"They call themselves *comuneros*."

"And they are ready . . ."

"They are already holding prisoner a handful of your friends, and our days are numbered. They will arrest us before they make their first move."

"You must be taken from here," Domingo Martínez said firmly. "I'll take you to my house. They don't suspect me."

"This is where I live," Cabeza de Vaca said. "This is where the Governor lives. And I'll stay here."

"But you can't! They've already set the day and the hour. It might be tomorrow or the day after. Let me hide you."

"I will not run away," Cabeza de Vaca said; he turned his face away from his friends and toward the crucifix on the wall.

The calendar was blurred. He had to move closer to it to see what day it was, but with each movement, his limbs seemed to die a little more. He edged his spent body across the bed until he could finally make it out. The uncrossed day was April 25. Tomorrow, then, would be St. Mark's day. Had he slept again through the morning and the afternoon? The sun was low, and he kept his eyes on the red disk until it disappeared over the ledge of the window. If only he could have some of his strength back.

A noise! Was it thunder? But he had just seen the sun set, and the sky was clear except for red patches. Why was the noise so much like thunder? It grew nearer and now he could tell that it came from a crowd. A great, one word shout seemed to float closer and closer until it exploded into the dark room:

"*Libertad!*"

Again and again, like a cannon now, that single word, *freedom*. The steps came with it, so loud, thumping into his brain. He shouted himself, for his servant, an old Basque.

"Bolt the door!"

His hands reached the bedpost, and he pulled himself up, all his strength in his arms. He saw the servant go to the door of the house. But instead of locking it, he flung it open, and the darkness of the evening was suddenly torn by torches. He saw their faces in that light, faces and swords, one as deadly as the other. He fell back on his pillow and begged God to forgive him for not being able to stand up to his assassins.

"Why don't you kill me?" he asked; but he was not sure that he had spoken. Daggers, not one, but many, were at his throat and at his bare chest, cooling blades against the hotness of his body.

He had closed his eyes against the impact of the hatred in their eyes and opened them only when he felt himself being dragged from his bed. His head must have hit something. It must have been the floor, for he saw their boots, the leather worn, in shreds, and some bare feet. They jerked him up by his arms, and he was grateful that his feet were touching the ground. He tried to walk, but he could not keep up with their pulling and pushing. That single word *"Libertad!"* seemed to drill a wound into him.

"To Garcí-Vanega's house!" someone shouted.

He was not sure, but he thought he heard swords crash. Was there someone fighting for him? Once, when he fell, his hand brushed against a sticky wetness; and when he brought it up to the light of the torch, he saw it was blood. He hoped it was his own.

He fainted then; and when he came to, he was in a small windowless room. A closet perhaps. Yet he was on a cot. When he tried to raise himself up, he realized that his hands were held fast behind his head. His wrists and his legs were enclosed in iron. Outside he recognized the voice of the clerk, Bartolemé Gonzales:

"Now, gentlemen, shout all together: *Libertad!*" Before fainting again he felt a wave of pity for them. To heed a command like that, meant giving up all freedom, even their kind of freedom.

"He was just a beggar!" One of the guards, and there were five of them in the tiny room, spat; and the spit landed on the chains that held him to the bed.

"You'd think a governor would have *something!*" another soldier said disdainfully.

"And what did they find in his house? A white candle, half-burned; a sailmaker's needle, and broken at that; a metal syringe; and a single, good suit of clothes."

"That was his court suit. With it he was going to impress the ruler of *El Dorado.*"

They all roared with laughter.

"Don't forget his papers!" Another soldier snickered and shifted his sword to his left hand.

"Ah, yes! His precious papers! A notebook about his family, and that book of his on that foolish expedition to Florida."

"They burned them along with those reports in which he accused all of us of not loving the redskins like he does."

He wished he had remained unconscious. He wished he had not heard about his papers. Sometimes when he had felt especially lonely, he had read about his ancestors. And he used to re-read his published journal. Reading it gave him more pleasure than he cared to admit.

"Have you heard?" The voices never stopped. The guards were not the only ones in his prison. Soldiers and settlers came in to look at him in irons and to bring more news, news of new outrages, new crimes. "Cabeza de Vaca's judge, the one he appointed, got beaten with his rod of justice. Now the symbol of our dear Governor's rule has found some real use."

"I saw the judge being pulled by his beard to Cabrera's house."

"My friend, Manolo, whom he put in jail because he killed an Indian, is out, free."

"But the jail isn't empty. They've rounded up all the constables and put them there."

He heard them tell that his notary, Pedro Hernandez, would not surrender the testimonies he had taken against Irala; Hernandez had been beaten and thrown in jail. Others who came to see their former governor bragged about the number of slaves they would have, with Irala governing the city. All through a nightmarish night Cabeza de Vaca heard reports of how the little law and order and justice he had built into the city and into the minds of its people were being destroyed.

By morning the insurgents held captive all those who were not with them openly. The Indians were paralyzed with terror at the white man's anger and hatred, which had turned the city in the wilderness into a place of wild anarchy.

16

The night of the rebellion, Irala was absent from the streets of Asunción. When the shouting died down, the men, exhausted by their work of overthrowing a government went to sleep and Irala began the job of legalizing the revolt.

Late the next afternoon he gathered all the settlers in front of the cathedral and read to them the legal document he had drawn up.

"Since Alvar Núñez Cabeza de Vaca threatened the settlers of Asunción with an autocratic rule, which would have deprived them of their possessions and ultimately would have turned the Spaniards into his slaves, the people of Asunción in the interest of liberty itself, have placed the Governor under arrest."

"Death to the tyrant!" someone shouted, and the shout was picked up by the others. Irala held up his hand for silence.

"He is a very sick man," he told them, "He will probably die without any help from us."

"Irala for governor!" someone shouted. And that shout could not be silenced by Irala, no matter how many times he raised his hands. So that day he had himself elected governor. His stoutest friends were placed in positions of power, and in his inaugural address he promised the settlers everything they wanted:

"You will have slaves, and you will have freedom. I will give you a rule of understanding. No man, no Spaniard, need fear in Asunción ever again. And gold we shall have! Enough for all of us and for our king."

Seeing their eagerness to know about what was in store for their ex-governor, he assured them that he was quite safe:

"There are four padlocks on his door and fifty men guarding him around the clock. Around his prison we have driven stakes into the ground, stakes that go six feet deep, so no friend of his, not even a rat, can dig a tunnel to him. Every house nearby has been searched and will be searched for as long as he lives. We have made him as comfortable as we can. There is grass growing under his bed to remind him of his forest friends. And I have personally seen to it that he has candles, should he need them for his last rites."

But no man, if he is successful, is without enemies. And there were still people, outside of the jail who did not condemn Cabeza de Vaca. They did not like Irala's cunning. He had lost their trust a long time before and he had done nothing to regain it and much to increase it. But they kept their feelings to themselves. Some of them, however, were willing to take a chance and let Cabeza de Vaca know how they felt. Among these was, of course, Domingo Martínez.

The man who was in charge of guarding Cabeza de Vaca was chosen for his job because he had a personal reason for violently hating the Governor. Hernando de Sosa had once struck an Indian chief, and Cabeza de Vaca had struck him back in front of everyone, Indians and Spaniards. Even de Sosa's friends had laughed at him; and he knew that news of his disgrace would always travel wherever he might go, and would one day return to Spain with him. Now that same de Sosa stood at Cabeza de Vaca's bedside.

It was de Sosa himself who examined the old Indian woman who, twice a day, brought in the prisoner's food. He stripped her naked, looked into her mouth and ears, and the first day even shaved her head to make his daily searches easier. Yet the Governor, guarded as he was, received almost daily communications from those who were opposed to Irala. And he, the Governor, in turn sent messages back.

It was the Governor's ingenious friend, Domingo Martínez who had devised a way for the Indian woman to carry those messages—a way, which was to be used, four centuries later, by the great Houdini. The messages were written on extremely thin paper and covered with black wax. Folded and re-folded, they were then placed under the woman's toes and attached to them with black threads. In this way the old woman was also able to smuggle in a black powder, which when diluted with saliva, served Cabeza de Vaca for ink. While the Governor ate, the old woman stood by his bed and scratched herself. She scratched her shaved head and her back and even her toes. As she took the tray away her hand would meet the Governor's and the messages and written supplies would be passed to him and his messages would be handed to her.

In this way Cabeza de Vaca found out that his friends in prison were willing to die with him, and those on the outside were willing to live and carry on his work. He also found out how dreadful things were under Irala's rule. A man who had killed his own daughter went free. Pedro de Molina, a judge under Cabeza de Vaca, had publicly demanded of a notary that "murders, evils, and injustices occasioned by the arrest of Cabeza de Vaca should cease." He called for the release of the Governor and the deposition of Irala. When the notary refused to read a document to this effect to the assembled people, Molina handed him his sword and woolen cap, a fee which obliged the public servant to read the document. The notary began to mumble the words, and Molina ordered him to read louder. Finally he grabbed the document and read it himself to the assembled settlers. He was beaten brutally and thrown into jail.

Cabeza de Vaca learned that his followers had been deprived of their property and tortured in jail. Testimony was being taken against him with the help of a giant wooden screw, which twisted the legs of those unwilling to bear false witness. He wrote back to his supporters, imploring them not to take risks and begging them to "be calm and quiet, for I am more afflicted by the scandals and disorders than by my cruel imprisonment."

If the Spaniards fared badly, the Indians, following the loss of his freedom, lost all of theirs. They were a forgotten people, remembered only when they possessed something worth stealing. Every Indian was someone's slave, and there was no one to whom any could turn for protection. The Spaniards became more cruel with each passing day.

One day Alonso de Cábrera, Garcí-Vanegas, and a notary came into the Governor's cell.

"We want you," Cábrera said without any preliminaries, "to formally appoint Domingo de Irala as your lieutenant."

"Giving him," Vanegas added, "full powers over the colony for the duration of your illness."

"My imprisonment, you mean," Cabeza de Vaca said.

"The notary will take it all down," Cábrera said soberly, motioning to the notary to get ready with a pad and pencil.

"What is Irala now but a self-styled governor?" Cabeza de Vaca said, and there was amusement in his voice. "Why would he want me to abdicate?"

"We came here to ask you for a legal document, not to answer your questions or hear your opinions." Cábrera shouted angrily.

"Crimes cannot be made legal through notaries," Cabeza de Vaca said calmly and turned his head away from them.

"This is your last chance," Vanegas said.

Cabeza de Vaca raised himself as high as he could.

"Take this down," he said to the notary. "I, Alvar Núñez Cabeza de Vaca, appointed by His Majesty Governor of Asunción and all the lands of Paraguay, name as His Majesty's proxy . . ." he waited for the notary to catch up with him, "with full powers, to govern in my name, this colony during my illness . . . Captain Juan de Salazar."

The paper was snatched from the notary by two pairs of hands, and the door was slammed off its hinges.

But Pedro Hernandez, the Governor's legal notary, was now free; and Cabeza de Vaca's appointment of Salazar was smuggled to him under the old Indian woman's toes.

They kept him chained only during the day and took the irons off his arms while he ate and slept. Since he knew they wished him dead, and since he was slowly getting over his sickness and would not die of natural causes, he began to fear that his food might be poisoned. As he later testified, "so for many days I did not dare to eat the meat and fish they gave me, but only the bread and some fruits in which they could not put poison." They tried other ways of killing him, but none of them drastic enough. No one wanted to be accused of his murder. So they set fires around his prison, hoping that the wind would be the culprit. They waited for him to get out of bed and start walking around so that they could lay traps for him. And they stayed awake nights thinking of other ways to bring about death without assassination.

But if men feared to openly assassinate their legal Governor, this was the only thing they feared. In

Asunción there was no pretense of justice. Private vendettas were carried on openly and on a daily basis. If a man wanted what belonged to another, he just took it, killing or maiming if necessary. Irala himself set an example of lawlessness by pursuing an enemy into the interior of a church and pushing a priest aside to lay his hands on the man he wanted punished. His own servant, Juan Viscaino, openly swore during mass; and when someone objected to this insult to God, Viscaino slew the man at the altar and went unpunished.

There was an atmosphere of discontent, distrust, uneasiness and even fear everywhere. It was as if a permanent shadow obscured the sun; as if punishment was being awaited by all. And this feeling was with Irala more than anyone.

"He is still haunting us," he shouted. "He's like a plague among us, festering discord."

He called his cabinet together to decide once and for all Cabeza de Vaca's fate. The act of murder, having been discussed many times and always rejected, was not brought up.

"There is only one way left to us." Irala finally said after having listened to many suggestions, none of them acceptable. "We must send him back to Spain . . ."

"To denounce us?" someone asked surprised.

"To stand trial!" Irala said calmly. A murmuring of voices greeted this announcement, and the cabinet broke into applause. "We have enough evidence to convict him."

"We have enough testimony," the notary shouted, "to sink the ship he'll be sailing on."

After the laughter subsided, one of the men asked:

"What will be the charges against him?"

"Assuming the King's own powers in Asunción!" Irala's voice was strong, and in the quiet room it rang out with such force that the sound of it frightened many. His shiny eyes looked from face to face, his penetrating gaze seemed to drill deeply into each soul. No one protested the accusation, and he went on. "We will accuse him of trying to make himself king in Asunción, of assuming such powers as belong only to His Majesty. That will be the principle charge. Other charges will also be brought. As you know, we have one document, with 232 signatures, which lists all of his crimes against the Crown and against us. We have enough testimony and witnesses to make a traitor of Alvar Núñez Cabeza de Vaca!"

There was only one more thing to be done, find and destroy any and all documents that might favor Cabeza de Vaca. But here again Domingo Martínez's ingenuity fouled up some well laid plans. He and other partisans of the Governor drew up testimonies not only defending Cabeza de Vaca against Irala's charges, but accusing Irala of sabotaging the Governor's rule, disobeying orders, breaking laws, and conspiring against the Crown. These papers Martínez wrapped in waxed cloth and hid in a piece of hollowed timber. Taking into his confidence one of the carpenters who was working on the ship that was to take the Governor to trial in Spain, Martínez saw that the documents were smuggled into the shipyard and the piece of timber was made a part of the ship's poop. A sailor was then sworn to secrecy; and he alone, of all the men who were to sail, knew the hiding place of the papers.

On the morning of March 7, 1545, almost a year after his imprisonment, Cabeza de Vaca was taken from his cell to the waiting ship. Almost every settler and every Indian in Asunción saw him being dragged through the streets to the ship. His friends had arranged for Juan de Salazar to stand nearby as the Governor boarded the vessel. Before his foot touched the gangplank, Cabeza de Vaca turned toward the crowd, his hand on the shoulder of the man he had chosen as his proxy.

"Sirs!" Cabeza de Vaca's voice carried loud and strong through the fresh morning air, to the farthest edge of the crowd. "Be my witnesses that I appointed, as my deputy, Juan de Salazar, that he should govern this province, instead of me, and in the name of His Majesty maintain order and justice till the King be pleased to make other disposition."

It had happened so fast, and his words so surprised those present that he was allowed to finish before Garcí-Vanegas rushed at him, a dagger raised high in his hand.

The calm in the eyes of the Governor infuriated Vanegas. He brought the dagger down, but did not dare aim it at Cabeza de Vaca's heart; for he did not wish to kill or to maim him; rather he wanted to frighten the man, make him fall to his knees. The sharp blade grazed the Governor's cheek and still his eyes were calm.

The crowd surged forward, and the men who held the Governor were pushed. Cabeza de Vaca fell, and for a moment, as he turned his bloodied face away from the ship and towards the people, there was an unbidden sympathy in some. But hands dragged him hastily aboard, the anchor was lifted, the gangplank pulled up, and the sails filled with wind. The crowd stood silent, watching the ship disappear in the tangle of green vegetation.

That night a handful of men gathered together in Domingo Martínez's house and talked about Cabeza de Vaca.

"What did he accomplish in the four years here?" someone asked, but it was not really a question for he went on speaking himself. "He did something quite extraordinary. He took the face of war in his hands and placed it on the altar of peace."

"The expedition to find *El Dorado?*"

"Yes, that expedition. He took with him the most warlike, the most bloodthirsty, the most cruel, and the most selfish from among us and led them on a journey of peace. And since he failed to change them, I believe that Christ Himself would not succeed today among the Spaniards!"

"But Cabeza de Vaca should never have come here," someone else said. "It was a wrong job for him. He had a sacred mission, an oath that he kept, to love and to help the Indians. But that was all he wished to do here. He left the natives aware of a good that can exist in Christians, a nobility of soul they never knew existed. But as Governor he could not have succeeded, not while he was the kind of man he was."

"The Indians are the only ones who understood him."

"And for that he is made to return to Spain in chains!" Martínez shouted banging his wrist against the table. "No gentlemen! He has been jailed and already condemned, for being a failure! He is returning to Spain sick and penniless. His compassion and his love made an invalid of him, and his unwillingness to become like the rest of us made him a prisoner. Alvar Núñez Cabeza de Vaca has no place in this world. He is an obsolete man. And the world is the worse for it."

That same night, in the small cabin that was to serve as his prison through the long voyage, Cabeza de Vaca reexamined his life himself. He had been a prideful man, not wanting nor seeking anyone's advice, not interested in another's side. He had been a righteous man, an unbending man, a man of little compassion and little patience towards his countrymen. And indeed he had been a tyrant in pursuing his ideas of justice. He had taken more pains with the problems of the Indians than with the problems of the settlers. He had been guilty of all that, but he still did not believe that he had been wrong. He would fight back against the accusations, save his honor and return to the people who needed him most, the natives of South America.

But it was not that simple. He had no one to defend him. There was no one who knew what had really happened. Then the day before they left the Rio de la Plata, on April 20, 1545, a stone was tossed into his porthole by an invisible hand. The letter attached to the stone told Cabeza de Vaca of the documents that had been smuggled on board the ship. The knowledge that he was returning with some written evidence, gave him new hope. His mind could be at peace.

On the voyage, his enemies, especially Cabrera and Vanegas, who were in charge of bringing him to Spain, did not rest. The ship was searched thoroughly. Any and all documents that seemed favorable to Cabeza de Vaca were torn to bits, and the bits scattered into the ocean. Everyone was suspect. The sailors' bunks were turned upside-down, their conversations placed under scrutiny.

As the journey progressed Cabrera became more and more violent in his suspicions and fears. His rages went on far into the night; his angry shouts grew so loud they were painful to the ears. He was often seen stabbing his dagger and swinging his sword at imaginary enemies. The thin line that separated him from insanity was erased during a great storm that lasted four days.

As the first gigantic wave of the angry sea lifted them up to the darkening sky and hurled them down again into black space, Cabrera fell to his knees and screamed out his fear:

"It is your wrath, oh Lord! You are avenging Cabeza de Vaca!"

Still on his knees, while the ship tilted and righted itself, he crawled to the Governor's cabin and remained there, begging Cabeza de Vaca to forgive him and promising undying friendship.

"From this day on, I shall be your humble servant," he mumbled, hugging the Governor's chains. For four days he lay at his prisoner's feet and trembled at the sounds of the roaring seas and the raging skies. And then, the wind died, the sun came out, and the blue of a calm ocean stretched before them. Most of the supplies had been lost, either swept off the decks or soaked into uselessness. All aboard had to content themselves with dried fish and bread baked of corn flour. The planks of the ship were used for firewood, and water had to be rationed.

Cabrera recovered and once again began to plot. He took Hernandez to the Governor's cabin to stand witness to his good intentions. He promised Cabeza de Vaca that he would destroy all testimonies and documents denouncing him, if only the Governor would surrender, also for destruction, any documents he might have in his own defence. Cabeza de Vaca was never tempted to fall into the trap.

On July 16, two and a half months after its departure from Asunción, the ship touched a Portuguese Island, *Terceira Isla,* in the Azores. Here Vanegas and Cabrera took Cabeza de Vaca ashore to try to have him arrested by the Portuguese authorities.

"When Cabeza de Vaca sailed for Paraguay," Vanegas told the Justice there, "he landed at the Portuguese Island of Cabo Verde. There he stole land and valuable personal property from Portuguese citizens."

The Justice laughed. "My King is not a man to let things go that way," he said. "He does not neglect his ports in such a way that things can be stolen."

At this point, Cabeza de Vaca himself spoke and asked for asylum and a Portuguese vessel to take him to Spain.

"I do not trust my jailors," he told the Justice and his notaries, "to take me safely to Spain."

It is not clear whether or not asylum was granted. It is believed, however, that the packet of papers was extracted from the poop of the Spanish ship at this time, with Portuguese notaries as witnesses. If asylum was granted, Cabeza de Vaca probably sailed on a Portuguese vessel to Lisbon, and from there went on to Spain. Whatever happened a week after the stop at the Azores, Cabeza de Vaca once more set foot in his native land.

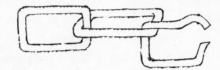

17

"That's the traitor!" The man pointed a finger, and his young son turned to look. "That's Alvar Núñez Cabeza de Vaca, the traitor of Paraguay! But what is he doing here? He is supposed to have deserted to the King of Portugual."

"What's a traitor?" the boy asked. The old man did not look harmful, but kindly. His white hair fell long on his shoulders, and his walk had seemed uncertain when his father spoke. But now he walked away from them, very straight, tall, and proud.

When he overheard the man, Cabeza de Vaca had just left the boat that had brought him to the port city of Cadíz. He was on his way to the King's representative to ask for the arrest of Cabrera and Vanegas. In just one week the lies of his jailors had traveled from Seville, where they had landed, to Cadíz. How many people in Spain were calling him a traitor, he, who once had been a hero?

Downcast already when he approached the authorities, he was more downcast when he left. They refused to arrest Cabrera and Vanegas; and what is more, it was now plain that it was he, not his enemies, who would stand trial.

He turned and tossed on his bed that night; sleep would not come. How could they accuse him? How could they believe the lies against him? Why did no one understand? If he had failed as governor in finding gold, did that mean he had failed at everything? What about the Indians? Didn't anyone understand what he had done for them? And hadn't the King himself made laws against the enslavement of the natives? Yet, there were slaves all over Spain. Slaves from the Indies; and men made money buying and selling them. Such men were against him, would always be against him. And others, too, would be: those who did not know the truth; those who would not see the truth; and those to whom truth was of no importance.

When the morning sun at last lighted the window, he sighed. There were no answers to his questions. Perhaps evil always came from good. If that was so, then there was no help for him. But he would not give in without a fight. His resources might be few, but the strength of right was on his side. Of that he was sure.

He was no stranger to fighting, although he had always wanted to be a man of peace. But this he hoped would be his very last fight. He would clear his name, bring to the Council of the Indies the truth that he had lived by. And then, he would go back. He would go back to Paraguay and make it the greatest of all colonies, a colony of peace and prosperity. Victory had to be his, because, just as there is a morning after night, the righteous must be victorious in the end.

The case against the Governor was prepared by Marcelo de Villalobos, a brilliant lawyer. Cabeza de Vaca, in the meantime, drew his own counter-accusations for the Council of the Indies, based on the papers that had been saved.

On January 20, 1546, in Madrid, those allowed inside the courtroom of the Council listened to Villalobos's summation of his case against the Governor of Paraguay. The desk in front of the barrister was covered with the papers.

"The charges against Alvar Núñez Cabeza de Vaca," Villalobos began, "number thirty-five. They are substantiated by signatures of nearly three hundred settlers of Asunción."

He waved the infamous document. Cabrera was not there to testify; he was insane. The charges themselves, the bulk of them, and signatures, not witnesses, had to suffice to convict the Governor.

Cabeza de Vaca listened, first with disbelief, then with growing indignation and anger to the charges:

"The accused repeatedly tried to usurp His Majesty's authority. Once he removed from a ship the King's arms and flew his own device, that of a cow's head. This device the Governor also wished to use as currency. He called himself king and repeatedly declared: 'I am prince and master of this land!' He fired His Majesty's tax collector and changed the tax regulations in order to gain profit for himself. Further to profit by his position, he allowed no one to trade with the Guaranís but his own servants, thus gaining great wealth and depriving the settlers of their livelihood. He once delivered twenty-five friendly Indians to be killed and eaten by another tribe. His acts of cruelty and presumption are numerous. They are all cited here and sworn to by witnesses. Even his own friends found it necessary to testify against him.

"There can be no doubt in your minds, your honors, of the guilt of this man; this man who defrauded the Crown by his inability to conduct an expedition to *El Dorado;* this man who, named Governor of a new land, did everything in his power to profit by his position and nothing to help develop the colony; this man whose very friends had to turn away in shame at the excesses of his reign, the discord he sowed, the demoralization he perpetrated.

"I ask the Council to require the accused to right the wrongs he committed, to impose on him a fine of 100,000 ducats to be paid to the Royal Treasury, and if he should refuse, to imprison him in order to set an example for others who would cheat the Crown and sin against Spain's brave colonists."

Not allowed to present his counter-accusations and unwilling to speak in his defence, for he did not wish to even acknowledge the accusations, Cabeza de Vaca was sentenced by the Council of the Indies to a public jail. This hasty and unjust decision was reversed on April 19, when he was allowed to leave prison for private residence, pending a further hearing. He was, however, restricted to the house, therefore under house arrest.

175

Days of agony had taken their toll in Cabeza de Vaca's appearance. When he and his lawyer, Alonzo de San Juan, entered the courtroom for the new hearing, he looked like a different, much older man. Lines were etched deeper in his face; bluish shadows were immobile around brows and cheeks; the greyness of his complexion was lighted only by the burning fire of his eyes. But pain adds nobility to any face, and Cabeza de Vaca had always had a noble face; now a force seemed to have been unleashed that made his look almost one of grandeur.

For two days the court heard his case, pitifully meager in documentation, with not a single witness to support it. Those who sat in judgment wanted to hear him disprove his guilt, if he could. Instead, what they heard was not really a defence but a testament of beliefs, a recitation of what he had hoped to do, a litany of his aims, a commentary on his unrealized dreams, a listing of injustices committed by his accusers, a blueprint for the brotherhood of man.

The judges heard everything he said; they sensed the honesty of the man. But what of testimony, what of witnesses? Those who accused Cabeza de Vaca had prepared their case well. The defendant had not.

"Guilty on the ground of an insufficient number of witnesses," the judges declared.

"You're sentencing this man," Alonzo de San Juan cried, "because the lies and the liars overweigh one man and the truth. I ask time for my client to procure witnesses."

"Granted."

So it was not enough to be an honest man. One needed signatures to testify to that, witnesses to back the truth. One needed more friends than one had enemies.

It was impossible to send for anyone from Asunción. They had to content themselves with the few who were available, in Spain: Pedro Hernandez, his faithful notary; Pedro Estopinan Cabeza de Vaca, who was in Asunción with him but who, as a kinsman was thought prejudiced; Juan de Salazar de Espinosa, to whom Cabeza de Vaca had wished to delegate his powers; a monk, Friar Alonso de Medina; and three sailors who knew of the treatment of the Indians by the settlers.

Although only seventy-six questions were asked of these witnesses, their testimonies substantiated everything Cabeza de Vaca had said and refuted all of his accusers' lies. His character and policies were vindicated. Yet there still remained the document with the numerous signatures. The judges continued to be impressed by it and still held it valid, in spite of sworn testimony that the signatures were obtained by force and bribery. The judges were divided among themselves, they agreed only on postponing their verdict.

"We shall abstain," they announced, "from our decision for a period of three years."

For three years, then, the shadow of guilt was to hang over his head. For three years the gossip was to multiply and spread. For three years he would have no peace.

With each passing week those who were interested in his case grew more bored with it. With each passing month his figure, the tired body, the aging face, became more and more pathetic. And with each passing year what seemed no longer of any importance to anyone grew gigantic in importance to the man himself.

By the end of three years Irala had united Paraguay and Peru. He was sending urgent messages to the King: "Though we shall have to strip the fittings of our swords to make nails, we are bound to send back a ship of gold." Although merely promises, the impression was made that Irala had succeeded where Cabeza de Vaca had failed. The golden kingdom was as elusive as ever, it was never found; but along with Irala's optimistic reports, went letters from the settlers praising him as a true leader "for whom we all would gladly die." And the judges of the Council of the Indies read all those documents and were impressed, for the present is a greater force than the past, and grievances have less appeal than promises of accomplishment.

Only God seemed to be on Cabeza de Vaca's side during those desperate years. The prosecutor, Villalobos, died in 1551 in great poverty; Cabrera, in a fit of madness killed his own wife; Vanegas fell ill and died of suffocation.

Finally, on March 18, 1551, in Valladolid, the court convened for the third time to render a verdict in the case of Alvar Núñez Cabeza de Vaca, Governor of Asunción. And the verdict was more cruel than anyone had expected. They condemned him for all his acts, stripped him of his office of Governor, forbade him to ever hold any office in the Indies, exiled him to Algeria, where he was to serve for five years with his arms and horse at his own expense, and demanded that he pay restitution to any and all persons he had injured. Pending the execution of the verdict, he was, once again, thrown into jail.

If there had existed any hope in his heart, there was

none now. Self-pity began to grow in him, and with its growth, his pride began to die. He appealed the verdict, asked for his release from prison, and sent to the Council a letter that even a year before he would not have brought himself to write:

"I have no means to buy food nor to prosecute my case, and I am much in debt for all I spent for my fleet and to bring help to the lands whose officials seized me and sent me back naked . . . I swear by God and by His cross that I know of no one who will lend me anything because my poverty is notorious."

The Council's answer was to state again its verdict. But it was the King, himself, who, hearing the severity of Cabeza de Vaca's sentence, reversed the Council's decision. The King absolved him from service in Africa and from payment of any kind of indemnities, freed him from imprisonment, but re-affirmed his perpetual banishment from the Indies.

He was sixty when he walked away from his last prison. His will to fight, in order to clear his name, was with him still. Once again pride filled his emaciated body. It was all he had left. On November 25, 1551, he demanded that the Council once again open his case to allow him an examination of all testimonies against him. His appeal was dismissed. The case was eleven years old, and the Council had grown weary of it.

Ill, penniless, and broken-hearted Cabeza de Vaca busied himself with a revision of his *Relatiónes* and an account of his governorship, which was published for the first time in 1542. Each word of it as he wrote, opened old wounds and inflicted new ones. Was it wrong to walk alone through life? Was it wrong to adhere to one's own sense of justice and accept no one else? Was justice and truth something personal? Certainly failure was; no one shared in that. And pride, that was also a personal thing. And suffering and pain and poverty and debasement and pity: those were personal things. But neither truth nor justice should be. They touch all men and must be part of mankind.

He was alone with his doubts, with his arguments, with himself and his memories, reliving his life over and over again. He was forgotten now, an old man with a faraway look. He was very thin and very tall, and children who saw him walk uncertainly over the paved streets and with a surer step over the naked earth, could not tell if he was sad or just very old.

He died in 1556, and there was no one but a priest at his side. But just before he died he knew peace. He found his peace in a belief that he would soon be with God.

Bibliography

Baker, J. N. L. *History of Geographical Discovery and Exploration.* Boston: Houghton Mifflin, 1931.

Bancroft, Hubert Howe. *History of Central America,* Vols. 6-8. San Francisco: The History Company, 1883-87.

———. *History of Texas,* Vol. 15. San Francisco: The History Company, 1886.

Bandelier, Adolph F. *Hemenway Southwestern Archeological Expedition: Contributions to the History of the Southwest Portion of the United States.* Cambridge: J. Wilson & Son, 1890.

———. *Papers of the Archeological Institute of America; American Series iii-iv: Final report of investigations among the Indians of the southwestern United States, carried on mainly in the years from 1880-1885.* Cambridge: J. Wilson & Son, 1890-92.

Bandelier, Fanny, trans. *The Journey of Alvar Núñez Cabeza de Vaca.* New York: A. S. Barnes, 1905.

Baskett, James N. "Study of the Route of Cabeza de Vaca," *Texas State Historical Quarterly,* Vol. 10.

Bishop, Morris. *The Odyssey of Cabeza de Vaca.* New York: Century, 1933.

Bolton, Herbert E., ed. *Spanish Exploration in the Southwest.* New York: Charles Scribner's Sons, 1916.

Brebner, J. B. *The Explorers of North America.* London: A. & C. Black Ltd., 1933.

Cabeza de Vaca, Alvar Núñez. *La Relación y comentarios.* Valladolid, 1555.

———. *Historiadores primitivos de las Indias Occidentales.* Madrid, 1749.

Castaneda, Pedro de. "Narrative of the Expedition of Coronado," *The Journey of Coronado.* Translated and edited by G. P. Winship. U.S. Bureau of American Ethnology 14th Annual Report, Part I (Washington, 1896), pp. 329-613.

Davenport, Harbert. "Expedition of Panfilo de Narvaez," *Southwestern Historical Quarterly*, Vols. 27-8.

Díaz del Castillo, Bernal. *True Conquest of New Spain*. New York: R. M. McBride, 1927.

Fiske, John. *The Discovery of America*. Boston and New York: Houghton Mifflin, 1892.

Hallenbeck, Cleve. *Alvar Núñez Cabeza de Vaca*. Glendale: Arthur H. Clark, 1940.

Hodge, Frederick W., and Lewis, T. H., eds. *Spanish Explorers in the Southern United States*, 1528-43. New York: Charles Scribner's Sons, 1907.

Kirkpatrick, R. A. *The Spanish Conquistadores*. London: A. & C. Black Ltd., 1934.

Las Casas, Bartolomé de, *Historia de las Indias*. Madrid: Academy of History, 1874.

———. *An Account of the First Voyages and Discoveries Made by the Spaniards in America*. London: D. Brown & A. Bell, 1699.

Lowery, Woodbury. *Spanish Settlements in North America*. New York: G. P. Putnam's Sons, 1905.

McFarland, Bates H. "Alvar Núñez Cabeza de Vaca," *Texas State Historical Quarterly*, Vol. I.

Martin, P. S. *Indians Before Columbus*. Chicago: University of Chicago Press, 1947.

Pninton, Brownie. "Alvar Núñez Cabeza de Vaca," *Texas State Historical Quarterly*, Vol. I.

Priestley, H. I. *The Coming of the White Man*. New York: Macmillan, 1929.

Richman, I. B. *The Spanish Conquerors*. New Haven: Yale University Press, 1921.

Rodman, Selden. *Haiti: The Black Republic*. New York: Devon-Adair, New Rev. Ed., 1961.

———. *Mexican Journal*. New York: Devon-Adair, 1958.

Smith, Buckingham, *Narrative of Alvar Núñez Cabeza de Vaca*. Washington, D.C., 1851.

Wells, Joseph K. "First Europeans in Texas," *Southwestern Historical Quarterly*, Vol. 22.